4TH– 6TH GRADE

Talksheets

ZONDERVAN/YOUTH SPECIALTIES BOOKS

Professional Resources

Advanced Peer Counseling in Youth Groups
Called to Care
The Church and the American Teenager
Developing Student Leaders
Feeding Your Forgotten Soul
Great Fundraising Ideas for Youth Groups
Help! I'm a Volunteer Youth Worker!
High School Ministry
How to Recruit and Train Volunteer Youth Workers
   (Previously released as Unsung Heroes)
Junior High Ministry (Revised Edition)
The Ministry of Nurture
Organizing Your Youth Ministry
Peer Counseling in Youth Groups
Road Trip
The Youth Minister's Survival Guide
Youth Ministry Nuts and Bolts

Discussion Starter Resources

Amazing Tension Getters
Get 'Em Talking
High School TalkSheets
Hot Talks
Junior High TalkSheets
More High School TalkSheets
More Junior High TalkSheets
Option Plays
Parent Ministry TalkSheets
Teach 'Toons
Tension Getters
Tension Getters Two

Special Needs and Issues

The Complete Student Missions Handbook
Divorce Recovery for Teenagers
Ideas for Social Action
Intensive Care: Helping Teenagers in Crisis
Rock Talk
Teaching the Truth About Sex
Up Close and Personal: How to Build
   Community in Your Youth Group

Youth Ministry Programming

Adventure Games
Creative Programming Ideas for Junior High Ministry
Creative Socials and Special Events
Good Clean Fun
Good Clean Fun, Volume 2
Great Games for City Kids

Great Ideas for Small Youth Groups
Greatest Skits on Earth
Greatest Skits on Earth, Volume 2
Holiday Ideas for Youth Groups (Revised Edition)
Junior High Game Nights
More Junior High Game Nights
On-Site: 40 On-Location Youth Programs
Play It! Great Games for Groups
Play It Again! More Great Games for Groups
Super Sketches for Youth Ministry
Teaching the Bible Creatively
The Youth Specialties Handbook for
      Great Camps and Retreats

4th–6th Grade Ministry

Attention Grabbers for 4th–6th Graders
4th–6th Grade Talksheets
Great Games for 4th–6th Graders
How to Survive Middle School
Incredible Stories
More Attention Grabbers for 4th–6th Graders
More Great Games for 4th–6th Graders
More Quick and Easy Activities for 4th–6th Graders
Quick and Easy Activities for 4th–6th Graders
Teach 'Toons

Clip Art

Youth Specialties Clip Art Book
Youth Specialties Clip Art Book, Volume 2
ArtSource Volume 1 - Fantastic Activities
ArtSource Volume 2 - Borders, Symbols, Holidays,
   and Attention Getters
ArtSource Volume 3 - Sports
ArtSource Volume 4 - Phrases and Verses
ArtSource Volume 5 -
   Amazing Oddities and Appalling Images
ArtSource Volume 6 - Spiritual Topics
The Church Clip Art Book (Zondervan)
Youth Ministry Clip Art Book (Group)

Video

Next Time I Fall In Love Video Curriculum
Understanding Your Teenager Video Curriculum
Video Spots for Junior High Game Nights

4TH- 6TH GRADE

Talksheets

25 creative, easy-to-use discussions for upper elementary students

David and Kathy Lynn

Youth Specialties

Zondervan Publishing House
A Division of HarperCollinsPublishers

4th–6th Grade TalkSheets

Copyright © 1993 by Youth Specialties, Inc.

*Youth Specialties Books, 1224 Greenfield Drive, El Cajon, California 92021,
are published by Zondervan Publishing House, Grand Rapids, Michigan 49530*

ISBN 0-310-37491-X

*Edited by Noel Becchetti and Lory Floyd
Cover and interior designed by Church Art Works
Illustrations by Corbin Hillam*

Printed in the United States of America

93 94 95 96 97 98 / ML / 10 9 8 7 6 5 4 3 2 1

This book is dedicated to the following kids who helped with its creation:
Jeremy, Conor, Rick, Megan, Kimberly, Megan, Rachel, Ben,
Richard, Chris, R.C., Gabe, Clayton, Kyan, Lyle,
Jovan, Anthony, Stephanie, Sarah, Bruce, and Jonny.

Table of Contents

HOW TO USE TALKSHEETS

You have in your possession a very valuable book. It contains 25 instant youth group discussions for upper elementary grade students. Inside, you will find reproducible "TalkSheets" covering a wide variety of "hot topics," plus simple step-by-step instructions on how to use them. All you need for 25 thought-provoking meetings is this book and access to a copy machine.

Preadolescents are crying out for more meaningful discussions with adults on a variety of life issues that affect them. Stories about Noah's three sons or the five loaves and two fishes are not meeting the needs of today's 4th–6th graders. Your young people may look like little kids, but they are growing up faster than any generation before them. In *Zingers: 25 Real-life Character Builders* (Zondervan Publishing House, 1990), we outlined the "Growing Up Too Fast Syndrome" and explained how it has placed adult-strength pressure on kids. Today's young people need dialogue with Christian adults more than they need lectures and preaching; this interaction will help them make sense of today's confusing world. TalkSheets help you do just this.

TalkSheets are versatile and easy to use. They can be enjoyed in a group meeting, a Sunday school class, or during a Bible study group. They can be used in either small or large groups. The discussions they instigate can be as brief as ten minutes or as long as interest remains and time allows. You can build an entire Sunday school or group meeting around a single TalkSheet, or you can use TalkSheets to supplement other materials and resources you might be using. The possibilities are endless.

TalkSheets are much more than just another type of curriculum or workbook. They invite excitement and involvement in discussing important life issues and how they relate to the Christian faith. TalkSheets deal with key topics that young people want to talk about. With interesting activities, challenging questions, and eye-catching graphics, TalkSheets will capture the attention of your 4th–6th graders and will help them think and learn. The more you use TalkSheets, the more your young people will look forward to them.

TALKSHEETS ARE DISCUSSION STARTERS

Although TalkSheets can be used as curricula for your program, they are primarily designed to be used as discussion starters. Everyone knows the value of a good discussion in which young people are interacting with adults and one another. When they are talking about a given subject, they are most likely thinking seriously about it and trying to understand it better. They are formulating and defending their points of view and making decisions and choices. Discussion helps truth rise to the surface, making it easier for young people to discover it for themselves. This age group has for too long been spoon-fed the truth. Many of the TalkSheets found in this book will push kids to think about their faith in new ways that will help them grow closer to Christ. There is no better way to encourage learning than through discussion.

A common fear among youth group leaders reticent about leading a group of kids in discussion is "What if the kids in my group just sit there and refuse to participate?" It is because of this fear that many choose to use a spelled-out curriculum, show a video, or give a prepared lecture.

Usually when young people fail to take part in a discussion it's because they haven't had the time or the opportunity to organize their thoughts. Most kids haven't yet developed the ability to "think on their feet"—to be able to present their ideas spontaneously and with confidence. They are afraid to speak for fear they might sound stupid in front of their peers.

TalkSheets remove this fear. They offer a chance to interact with the subject matter in an interesting, challenging, and nonthreatening way *before* the actual discussion begins. Not only does this give them time to organize their thoughts and to write them down, but it also helps remove any anxiety they might feel. Most will actually look forward to sharing their answers and hearing others' responses to the same questions. They will be ready for a lively discussion.

A STEP-BY-STEP USER'S GUIDE

TalkSheets are very easy to use, but they do require some preparation on your part. Follow these simple instructions and your TalkSheet discussion will be successful:

Choose the right TalkSheet for your group. Each TalkSheet deals with a different topic. The one you choose will have a lot to do with the needs and the maturity level of your group. It is not necessary (or recommended) to use the TalkSheets in the order in which they appear in this book.

Try it yourself. Once you have chosen a specific TalkSheet, answer the questions and do the activities yourself. Imagine your students participating. This role-playing will give you first-hand knowledge of what you will be requiring of your kids. As you fill out the TalkSheet, think of additional questions, activities, and Scriptures.

Read the Leader's Instructions on the back of each TalkSheet. Numerous tips and ideas for getting the most out of your discussion are contained in the Leader's Instructions. Add your own thoughts and ideas. Fill in the date and the name of the group at the top of each leader's page to track the topics you have discussed with different groups of kids.

Remove the TalkSheet from the book. The pages are perforated along the left margins for easy removal. The information is easier to copy when removed. Before making copies, you might wish to "white out" (with liquid paper) the page number.

Make enough copies for everyone. Each student will need his or her own copy of the TalkSheet. This book makes the assumption that you have access to a copy machine. Only the student's side of the TalkSheet needs to be copied. The leader's material on the other side is just for you, the leader.

Keep in mind that you are able to make copies for your group because we have given you permission to do so. U.S. copyright laws have not changed. It is still mandatory that you request permission from a publisher before making copies of other published material. It is illegal not to do so. Permission is given for you to make copies of this material for your group only, not for every 4th–6th grade group in your city. Thank you for your cooperation.

Introduce the topic. In most cases, it is important to introduce or "set up" the topic before you pass out the TalkSheets to your group. Any method will do as long as it is short and to the point. Be careful not to overintroduce the subject—avoid using an introduction that is too "preachy" or that resolves the issue before you get started. The primary purpose of the intro-duction is to stimulate interest and instigate discussion. The simplest way to introduce the topic is verbally. You can tell a story, share an experience, or describe a conflict having to do with the subject. You might ask a simple question, such as "What is the first thing you think of when you hear the word _____ (whatever the topic is)?" After a few volunteers have answered, you could reply, "It sounds like we all have different ideas on the subject; let's investigate it a bit further." Distribute the TalkSheets and pens or pencils, and you are on your way.

There are, of course, many other possibilities. The introduction of the topic is left to your discretion and good judgment. You are limited only by your own creativity. Suggestions are offered in each TalkSheet, but they are not mandatory for success. Remember that the intro-duction is an integral part of each session. It helps set the tone and influences the kinds of responses you receive. Do not "load" the introduction to the point that the "answer" or your bias is revealed and the young people feel hesitant about sharing their own opinions.

Give students time to work on their TalkSheets. After your topical introduction, pass out a TalkSheet to each group member. Adult leaders also need copies and should fill them out as well. Each participant should have a copy of the Bible, as well as a pen or a pencil. There are usually five or six activities on each TalkSheet. If time is limited, direct your kids' interest to the specific part of the TalkSheet that you want them to discuss.

Decide whether or not they should complete the TalkSheet on an individual basis or in groups.

Encourage your students to consider what the Bible has to say as they complete their TalkSheets.

Announce a time limit for their written work, then make them aware when one or two min-utes remain. They may need more or less time. Use your own judgment, depending upon your observations of the majority of the group. You are now ready to begin the discussion.

Lead the discussion. For the TalkSheet discussions to be effective, all members of your group need to be encouraged to participate. Foster a climate that is conducive to discussion by communicating that each person's opinion is worthwhile and that each has a responsibility to contribute to the rest of the group. A variety of opinions is necessary for these TalkSheets to have meaning.

If your group is large, you may want to divide it into small groups of four to six kids each. One person in each small group should be appointed facilitator to keep the discussion alive. The facilitator can be an adult or a young person. Advise the leaders not to dominate the group, but to be on the same level with each member. If the group looks to the facilitator for the "answer," have the leader direct the questions or responses back to the group. Once the groups have completed their discussions, have them reassemble into one large group. Move through the items again, and ask the different groups to summarize what they learned from each activity.

It is not necessary to divide up into groups every time TalkSheets are used. Variations provide more interest. You may prefer, at times, to have smaller groups of the same sex.

The discussion should center around the questions and answers on the TalkSheet. Go through them one at a time, asking volunteers to share their responses to each item. Have them compare their answers and brainstorm new ones to add to those they wrote down. Let those who don't feel comfortable revealing their answers remain silent.

Be sure your examples are concrete and specific for this age group. Preadolescents are aware of concepts like faith, but they are not yet equipped to comprehend them on an abstract level. They especially appreciate examples in the form of stories.

Don't feel pressured to spend time on each activity. If time does not permit a discussion of every item, feel free to focus attention only on those provoking the highest degree of interest.

Move with your own creative instinct. If you discover a better or a different way to use the activity, do it. Don't feel restricted by the leader's instructions on the back of the TalkSheet. Use Scriptures that are not found on the TalkSheet, and add your own items. TalkSheets were designed for you to be able to add your own thoughts and ideas.

If the group begins digressing into an area that has nothing to do with the topic, guide it back on track. However, if there is a high degree of interest in this side issue, you may wish to allow the extra discussion. It may meet a need of many in the group and be worth pursuing. Kids respect spontaneity because it demonstrates that you care enough to listen to their needs. Take the discussion in a different direction altogether if that is where your group feels it needs to go. More information on leading discussions can be found in the next section.

Wrap up the discussion. This is your chance to challenge the group. When considering your closing remarks, ask yourself the following question: What do you want the group to remember from this experience? If you can answer in two or three sentences, then you have your closing remarks. It is important to bring some sort of closure to the session without negating the thoughts and opinions expressed by the group. A good wrap-up should affirm the group and offer a summary that helps tie the discussion together. Your young people should be left with the desire to discuss the issue further, either among themselves or with a leader. Tell your group members you are available to discuss the issue privately after the meeting. In some cases, a wrap-up may be unnecessary—just leave the issue hanging and bring it up again at a later date. This allows your young people to wrestle with the issues on their own. Later, resolutions can evolve.

HOW TO LEAD A TALKSHEET DISCUSSION

Today's young people are growing up in a world of moral confusion. The problem facing children and youth workers in the church is not so much how to teach the church's doctrines, but how to help kids make the right choices when faced with so many options. The church's response to this problem has traditionally been to indoctrinate—to preach and yell its point of view louder than the rest of the world. This kind of approach does not work in today's world. Kids in the upper elementary grades are hearing a variety of voices and messages, most of which are louder than those they hear from the church.

A TalkSheet discussion is effective for just this reason. While discussing the questions and activities on the TalkSheet, your young people will be encouraged to think carefully about issues, to compare their beliefs and values with others, and to learn to make the right choices. TalkSheets will challenge your group to evaluate, defend, explain, and rework their ideas in an atmosphere of acceptance, support, and growth.

CHARACTERISTICS OF A TALKSHEET DISCUSSION

Successful discussions—those that produce learning and growth—rarely happen by accident. They require careful preparation and sensitive leadership. Don't be concerned if you feel you lack experience at this time or if you don't have the time for a lengthy preparation. The more TalkSheet discussions you lead, the easier they will become and the more skilled you will be. It will help if you read the material on the next few pages and try to incorporate these ideas into your discussions.

The following suggestions will assist you in reaching a maximum level of success:

Create a climate of acceptance. Most kids are afraid to express their opinions because they are fearful of what others might think. Peer approval is paramount with 4th–6th graders, just as it is with teenagers. They are fearful of being ridiculed or of being thought dumb. They need to feel secure before they can share their feelings and beliefs. They also need to know they can share what they are thinking, no matter how unpopular or wild their ideas might be. If any of your students are subjected to put-downs, criticism, laughter, or judgmental comments by their peers, an effective discussion will not happen. If the kids know you or other adults will criticize their statements because they may differ from what you or the church teaches, they will keep their opinions to themselves.

For this reason, each TalkSheet begins with a question or an activity less threatening and more fun than some of the questions that follow. The first question helps the individuals become more comfortable with each other and with the idea of openly sharing their views.

When asking a question, even one that is printed on the TalkSheet, phrase it to evoke *opinions*, not *answers*. In other words, if a question reads "What should Alfredo have done in that situation?" change it to "What *do you think* Alfredo should have done?" The addition of the three words *do you think* makes the question a matter of opinion rather than a matter of knowing the "right" answer. When young people realize their opinions are all that are necessary, they will be more apt to feel comfortable and confident.

Affirm all legitimate expressions of opinion from your group members. Let each person know that his or her comments and contributions are appreciated and important. This is especially true for those who rarely participate. When they do, make a point of thanking them, in order to encourage them to share again. Keep in mind that affirmation does not necessarily mean approval. Affirm even those comments that seem like heresy to you. By doing so, you let the group know all participants have the right to express their ideas, no matter what they are. If someone does express an opinion that you believe is way off base and needs to be corrected, make a mental note of the comment and present an alternative point of view in a positive way in your concluding remarks. Don't attack or condemn the person who made the comment.

Discourage the group from thinking of you as the "authority" on the subject. Most of the time kids will think you have the right answer to every question and they will watch for your reaction, even when they are answering someone else's question. If you find the group members' responses are slanted toward your approval, redirect them to the whole group. You could say, "Talk to the group, not to me" or "Tell everyone, not just me."

It is important for you to try to let them see you as a facilitator—another member of the group who is helping make the discussion happen. You are not sitting in judgment of their responses, nor do you have the right answer to every problem. You want them to see the importance of working together with adults, rather than viewing you or other adults as all-knowing.

Actively listen to each person. God gave you one mouth and two ears. Good discussion leaders know how to listen. Your job is not to monopolize the discussion or to contribute the wisest words on each issue. Keep your mouth shut except when you are encouraging others to talk. You can express your opinions during your concluding remarks.

Do not force anyone to talk. Invite students to speak out, but don't attempt to force them to do so. Each member should have the right to pass.

Do not take sides during the discussion. You will have disagreements in your group from time to time and students who will take opposing viewpoints. Don't make the mistake of siding with one group or the other. Encourage all sides to think through their positions and to defend their points of view. You might ask probing questions to encourage deeper introspection of all ideas. If everyone seems to agree on a question, or if someone seems fearful of expressing a controversial point, it might be beneficial for you to play devil's advocate with some thought-provoking comments. This will force them to think. Do not, however, give them the impression that the "other" point of view is necessarily your own—remain neutral.

Do not allow one person (including yourself) to monopolize the discussion. Almost every group has one person who likes to talk and is perfectly willing to express an opinion on every question. Try to encourage everyone to participate.

Arrange the seating to encourage discussion. Theater-style seating, in rows, is not conducive to conversation. If you must use chairs at all, arrange them in a circular or semicircular pattern.

Occasionally, smaller groups of four to six are less threatening to young people, especially if there is a variety of maturity levels in the group. If you have 3rd–6th graders in the same group, it might be preferable to segregate them into 3rd–4th graders and 5th–6th graders.

Allow for humor when appropriate. Do not take the discussion so seriously as to prohibit humor. Most TalkSheets include questions that will generate laughter as well as some intense dialogue. Remember the KISMIF principle—Keep It Simple, Make It Fun.

Don't be afraid of silence. Many discussion leaders are intimidated by silence in the group. Their first reaction is to fill the silence with a question or a comment. The following suggestions may help you handle silence more effectively:

a. Learn to feel comfortable with silence. Wait it out for 30 seconds. Give kids a reasonable time to volunteer their responses. If you feel it is appropriate, invite a specific person to talk. Sometimes a gentle nudge is all that is necessary.

b. Discuss the silence with the group members. Ask them what the silence really means. Perhaps they are confused or embarrassed and don't feel free to share their thoughts.

c. Answer the silence with questions or comments about it. Occasionally, comments such as "It's a difficult issue to consider, isn't it?" or "It's scary to be the first to talk" may break the ice.

d. Ask a different question that might be easier to handle or that might clarify the one that has been proposed. But don't do this too quickly—wait a short while.

Try to keep the discussion under control (with room for flexibility). Frequently a discussion can become sidetracked onto a subject that you may not consider desirable. If someone brings up a side issue that generates a lot of interest, you will need to decide whether or not to pursue it to see where it leads or redirect the conversation back to the original subject. Sometimes it's a good idea to digress, especially if the interest is high and the issue is worth discussing. In most cases, however, it is advisable to say something like, "Let's come back to that subject a little later, if we have time. Right now, let's finish our discussion on . . ."

Be creative and flexible. Don't feel compelled to ask every question on the TalkSheet, one by one, in order. If you wish, ask only a couple of them or add a few of your own. The Leader's Guide may give you some ideas, but think of your own as well. Each question or activity may lead to several others along the same lines that you can ask during the discussion.

Be an "askable" discussion leader. Make certain your kids understand they can talk to you about anything and find concern and support, even after the TalkSheet discussion has been completed.

Know what your goals are. A TalkSheet discussion should be more than just a bull session. TalkSheets are designed to move the conversation toward a goal, but you will need to identify that goal in advance. What would you like the young people to learn? What truth would you like them to discover? What is the goal of the session? If you don't know where you are going, it is doubtful you will arrive.

GROUND RULES FOR AN EFFECTIVE TALKSHEET DISCUSSION

A few ground rules will be helpful before beginning your TalkSheet discussions. Rules should be kept to a minimum, but most of the time young people will respond in a positive manner if they know in advance what is expected of them. The following are suggested ground rules:

"What is said in this room stays in this room."

Confidentiality is vitally important to a healthy discussion. The only time it should be broken is if a group member reveals that he or she is going to harm himself or herself or another person—or if the student is being harmed.

"No put-downs."

Mutual respect is important. If someone disagrees with another's comment, he or she should raise a hand and express an opinion of the *comment,* but not of the person who made it. It is permissible to attack ideas, but not each other.

"There is no such thing as a dumb question."

Your kids and adult leaders must feel free to ask questions at any time. Asking questions is the best way to learn.

"No one is forced to talk."

Let all your students know they have the right to remain silent about any question.

"Only one person talks at a time."

This is a good way to teach young people mutual respect. Each person's opinion is worthwhile and deserves to be heard.

If members of the group violate these rules during the discussion or engage in disruptive or negative behavior, it would be wise to stop and deal with the problem before continuing.

"Everyone is a resource person."

This applies to the adults even more than the young people. Too often kids are seen as objects. The old adage, "Kids should be seen and not heard," still holds true in the minds of many adults. A TalkSheet discussion should not be a time where adults tell kids what to believe, only allowing kids to share so they feel cared about. Rather, a TalkSheet discussion is a time where kids and adults together can grow in Christ and in the application of the Christian faith to everyday life.

USING THE BIBLE WITH TALKSHEETS

Adults often begin discussions with young people assuming they believe the Bible has authority over their lives. Adults either begin their discussions with Scripture or quickly support their contentions with Bible verses. Young people of today often consider their life situations first, then decide if the Bible fits. TalkSheets have been designed to deliberately begin your discussion with the realities of the preadolescent world and then move toward Scripture. This gives you the opportunity to show them the Bible can be their guide and that God does have something to say that is applicable to their age level and their interests.

The last activity on each TalkSheet involves Scripture. These Bible references were selected for their relevance to each issue and for their potential to generate healthy discussion. They are not to be considered exhaustive. It is assumed you will add whatever Scriptures you believe are equally pertinent. The passages listed are only the tip of the iceberg, inviting you to "search the Scriptures" for more.

Once the Scriptures have been read aloud, ask your students to develop a biblical principle that can guide their lives. For example, after reading the passage from Matthew 11 on the topic of rejection ("Reject!"), the group may summarize by saying, "Jesus Christ promises to accept us for who we are no matter what we have said or done. No matter how hurt or how weary we are, we can find God's love in the arms of Christ."

Kids don't always know where the Scripture passages are located in their Bibles. You can use the TalkSheet as an opportunity for kids to gain the helpful skill of learning their way around their Bibles.

Kids often do better studying the Bible passages in small groups. You can ask them to get into groups to focus on how the Bible applies to the life issue you are discussing.

A WORD OF CAUTION . . .

Many of the TalkSheets in this book deal with topics that may be sensitive or controversial. Discussing subjects such as profanity or the satanic may not be appreciated by everyone in the church. Whenever you encourage discussion on such topics or encourage kids to express their opinions (on any subject), no matter how "off base" they may be, you risk the possibility of criticism from parents or other concerned adults in your church. They may believe you are teaching the young people heresy or questionable values.

The best way to avoid problems is to use good judgment. If you have reason to believe a particular TalkSheet is going to cause problems, it would be judicious to think twice before you use it. Sometimes the damage done by going ahead outweighs the potential good.

Another way to avoid misunderstandings is to provide parents and others to whom you are accountable copies of the TalkSheet before you use it. Let them know what you hope to accomplish and the type of discussion you will be encouraging.

It would also be wise to suggest your kids take their TalkSheets home to discuss them with their parents. They might want to ask their parents how they would answer some of the questions.

GETTIN' GOOD AT BEIN' GOOD

1 What would your school be like if not one kid cared about right and wrong? _____

_____

_____

_____

2 From the following list, pick the things you think are right and the things you think are wrong. (Check either the RIGHT or the WRONG column.)

	RIGHT	WRONG
a. Lying to parents	_____	_____
b. Copying someone's math homework	_____	_____
c. Smoking a cigarette	_____	_____
d. Forgetting to do a chore	_____	_____
e. Missing church	_____	_____
f. Gossiping about another kid	_____	_____
g. Acting up in class	_____	_____
h. Shoplifting	_____	_____
i. Hurting someone's feelings	_____	_____
j. Watching television	_____	_____
k. Always doing what you are told	_____	_____
l. Swearing	_____	_____
m. Teasing others	_____	_____

3 When you have to make a decision about right and wrong, what sources best help you make the decision? (Check your top two choices.)

___ A parent   ___ A best friend   ___ Rock stars
___ Another kid   ___ The Bible   ___ Television role models
___ Comic books   ___ A coach   ___ A Sunday school teacher
___ Christian adults ___ A grandparent   ___ The teachings of your church

4 If you ruled the world, how would you help people learn right from wrong?

_____

_____

5 Circle one of the following sets of numbers. The set you pick represents a Bible verse you will study. Your leader will tell you how to find your verse in the Bible.

1 19 97 10   **1 20 14 16**   **2 6 12 9**

Date Used: _____

Group: _____

GETTIN' GOOD AT BEIN' GOOD
Topic: Morality

Purpose of this Session:

Preadolescents in the 4th–6th grades begin to experiment with behaviors that conflict with the values they were taught as children. Kids need the opportunity to talk about right and wrong choices and their struggles in dealing with these choices. This TalkSheet offers the chance for kids and adults together to discuss right and wrong and the pressures placed on kids to do wrong.

To Introduce the Topic:

Make up a distorted Ten Commandments (Exodus 20:1–17). For example, the first commandment could say, "I am your God, but if you wish, you can put sports or television stars ahead of me." Read your distorted list to the kids, then explain that you are going to talk about right and wrong.

The Discussion:

Item #1: Kids generally respond to this question by saying their schools would be unsafe, totally mixed up, and crazy—the ultimate nightmare. People would hurt each other, nobody would learn anything, and so on. Make a list of all the responses.

Item #2: Some kids will want a middle ground between right and wrong—a sort-of-wrong category. Ask the kids to choose only between the two—RIGHT or WRONG. This forced choice gives you the opportunity to talk about how we know right from wrong. Ask the kids why they believe it is wrong to lie, cheat, and so on. Focus on the consequences of doing wrong, possibly referring back to the responses in Item #1. For areas like watching television, take the teachable opportunity to discuss how to choose good programs over bad. Explore with the group why wrong things sometimes look appealing.

Item #3: Ask the group members to choose both the best four sources and the worst.

Item #4: After the group has shared its views, discuss why God's Word is important in learning right from wrong. Explain that God gave us the Ten Commandments and other rules to protect us. Refer back to the distorted reading of the Ten Commandments from the introductory activity. Ask the kids what might happen if they lived out these distorted commands, and point out the negative consequences. Emphasize God's protective nature by looking at the fifth commandment (Exodus 20:12). God promises that kids will live long if they honor their fathers and mothers. If parents let kids do anything they want or if kids disregard their parents' rules, the result is rather obvious. Breaking this commandment puts a child's safety in jeopardy.

Item #5: Explain that the first number represents the Old or New Testament (1 = Old Testament; 2 = New Testament), the second number represents the book of the Old or New Testament, the third number locates the chapter, and the fourth number indicates the verse. The three verses in order are Psalm 97:10; Proverbs 14:16; and Romans 12:9. These verses warn us to hate what is evil. Ask the kids to share how Christians can hate evil and love good.

To Close the Session:

Point out that when we live by God's rules we do better than when we break his rules. Explain that Jesus summarized God's commandments into one word—love. Wrap up the lesson by reading and discussing Matthew 22:34–39.

REJECT!

1 Do you believe kids who usually get rejected at your school are treated fairly? (Check one.)

_____ **Most of the time**
_____ **Some of the time**
_____ **None of the time**

2 Have you ever been left out of the fun a group was having?

_____ **Yes** _____ **No**

3 From the following examples, circle the two worst ways of getting rejected.

a. Being the last person picked for a team

b. Having no one ask you to do something with them during recess

c. Being made fun of in front of more than one person

d. Getting blamed because your team lost

e. Having someone play a mean trick on you

4 He is standing by the backstop watching you and your friends start up a baseball game. Henry is very overweight and is never picked for a team, but he likes to watch. He hopes to some day be asked to play.

"Hey Fatso, wanna play with us?" yells one of your friends. Before Henry can answer, your friend yells again, "You can be home plate!"

Henry slowly turns and walks away with his head hung low.

Now that you have heard this, what will you do as Henry walks away?

_____

_____

_____

5 Read **Matthew 11:28–30** and answer the following question:

What do you think this Scripture passage teaches about rejection and

acceptance? _____

_____

_____

_____

REJECT!
Topic: Rejection

Purpose of this Session:

We all know kids can be cruel to each other, especially to their peers who stand out as different. Ridicule is heaped on the poor kid wearing the wrong clothes; on the odd-looking kid with the big nose, the chicken lips, or the wing ears; and on the kid who stutters or walks with a limp. This TalkSheet gets kids talking about rejection—a feeling they have all experienced to some degree.

To Introduce the Topic:

Ask the kids to tell a group story about school rejection. Begin the story by saying, "The first week of school started off . . ." then have different kids provide a sentence, continuing the story from student to student. You may have to step in periodically to get the story back on track. You only need to keep the story going long enough to get a picture of how your group relates to rejection.

The Discussion:

Item #1: Ask the group to describe the types of people who are rejected. They will describe anyone who, in their perception, is different. Talk about why some kids are treated unfairly. Do they deserve this unfair treatment? Discuss a particularly tough situation—the kid who has moved.

Item #2: This question establishes that most, if not all, of your group has experienced rejection. Focus here on how your group members felt about their own rejections. You may want to role-play some of these situations to help kids take different perspectives. If young people see situations from other viewpoints, they understand their rejection experiences better and are less likely to reject others.

Item #3: Talk with the kids about how they can respond if they are rejected in these ways. Discuss how they can respond if their peers reject others in these ways.

Item #4: Use this Zinger to discuss how kids can work against rejection and still keep their friends. Ask the kids if this is a realistic situation. How often do these kinds of things happen? Then look at their response options. If this happened to your kids, they could (a) ignore it, (b) make fun of Henry, (c) decide they don't want to be a part of the team, (d) talk with Henry later, (e) talk with the team later about accepting Henry, (f) storm off angry and quit the team, or (g) pressure the kid who said "Hey Fatso" to take it back. Brainstorm with the kids ways they can befriend and help those rejected by the group without losing their own friends.

Item #5: Point out that God is not in the rejection business. Explore the following questions with your group: What is the Christian's role in preventing rejection? How can Christians face rejection? How can the group support those who feel its hurt? How can the group support those who are trying to prevent rejection from happening to others?

To Close the Session:

Research indicates that kids are cruel and demeaning to others in order to build themselves up. Cliques of young people find acceptance in each other through rejecting outsiders who are different. For example, the player who made the joke about Henry in Item #4 did it to cover up his or her own inadequacies.

Explain to the kids that when we reject others, we are really saying that we can't handle our own faults, character defects, and sin. If we can find others who appear different than us and ridicule them, then we must be okay. But this is not true. All of us need the love and grace of Jesus Christ. Instead of rejecting others, we need to look at our own lives in relationship to Jesus Christ.

DOUBLE TOUGH

1 What is one choice that was tough to make when you were much younger?

[   ]

2 Look through the following list of situations. Place an E in front of the easiest situations to handle and place a T in front of the toughest situations to handle.

___ Asking for help with schoolwork
___ Getting into trouble and not knowing how to get out of it
___ Staying friends after an argument with a good friend
___ Dealing with a problem with a stepparent or parent
___ Being pressured to smoke cigarettes
___ Choosing how to spend money
___ Being picked on by a brother or a sister
___ Being talked into doing something you know is wrong
___ Being picked on at school
___ Being ridiculed because of your glasses or braces
___ Choosing what video movie to rent
___ Being bothered by a gang

3 Whom do you usually talk with when you are faced with a tough choice and you do not know what to do? (Check your top two choices.)

_____ A teacher _____ A friend your age _____ A parent or a stepparent
_____ A coach _____ An adult friend _____ A pet animal like a dog or a cat
_____ God _____ A brother or a sister _____ No one

4 Complete the following sentence: **If I face a tough decision and make the wrong choice, I will . . .** _____

_____

5 What do you like about making your own choices? _____

_____

6 Read the following scrambled verses found in **Proverbs 8:33–36** by using the numbers, beginning with #1. Then write out what you believe the passage means.

3. Blessed is the man who listens to me,
1. Listen to my instruction and be wise;
5. waiting at my doorway.
2. do not ignore it.
4. watching daily at my doors,

6. For whoever finds me finds life
9. all who hate me love death.
7. and receives favor from the Lord.
8. But whoever fails to find me harms himself;

_____

_____

Date Used: _____

Group: _____

DOUBLE TOUGH
Topic: Handling Tough Choices

Purpose of this Session:

It goes without saying that kids today have it tougher than past generations, so adults must equip them to face the tough choices. As much as possible, we need to protect young people from the culture while at the same time prepare them to live in a society that throws tough choices their way. One of the best strategies to accomplish this is dialogue with parents and other trustworthy adults. Use this TalkSheet to discuss the tough choices your kids face and how adults can help them navigate these bumpy waters.

To Introduce the Topic:

Ask the kids to list all the choices that they had to make to get to the meeting. Then tell them that you will be discussing the tough choices they face.

The Discussion:

Item #1: Here you have the opportunity to take the group's stress pulse and allow the kids to share that stress. Young people will share everything from very tough choices, like whom to live with after their parents divorce, to trading things with friends or working their VCRs. The vital point here is to validate as important all the choices kids have faced.

Item #2: Young people may ask "what if" questions. Tell them to work through these situations at face value. If there are any situations they wish to add, they can do so. As a group, determine what makes a situation easy or difficult to handle.

Item #3: You have an important opportunity here to encourage young people to talk with trustworthy adults when they face double tough situations. Keeping quiet about choices or only sharing them with peers can lead to bad decisions. That does not mean young people must tell adults everything, but tough issues need to be talked through with an adult. Go back to Item #2 and list the situations that are best talked about with an adult. Brainstorm other strategies kids can consider.

Item #4: Again, encourage young people to ask an adult for help, especially for the tough decisions. Give some examples and ask the kids for examples.

Item #5: During the preadolescent years, young people are given more freedom by their parents and teachers. Generally, they like this newfound freedom, but they are also concerned that they may make wrong choices. Discuss with them both the good and the bad consequences of decision making. Take the opportunity to talk about how God and our Christian values can direct us in making wise choices.

Item #6: The focus of Proverbs 8:33–36 on wisdom reinforces the need for young people to listen to trustworthy adults. Discuss how God's Word provides Christians with a road map that guides us through the tough choices. Another source of wisdom is the community called the church. And don't forget to talk about the importance of prayer. Young people who listen to adults, to the Bible, to God in prayer, and to the community of believers have a better chance of making wise choices.

To Close the Session:

If you feel comfortable with role-plays, you can play out different situations with volunteer young people. Ask each volunteer to choose a tough choice and come to you as the adult. These role-plays demonstrate the benefits of dialoguing with trustworthy adults. Your role-play need not be a lecture but a guided discussion where you ask a number of questions to help the young person make an informed choice.

FAMILY FRICTION

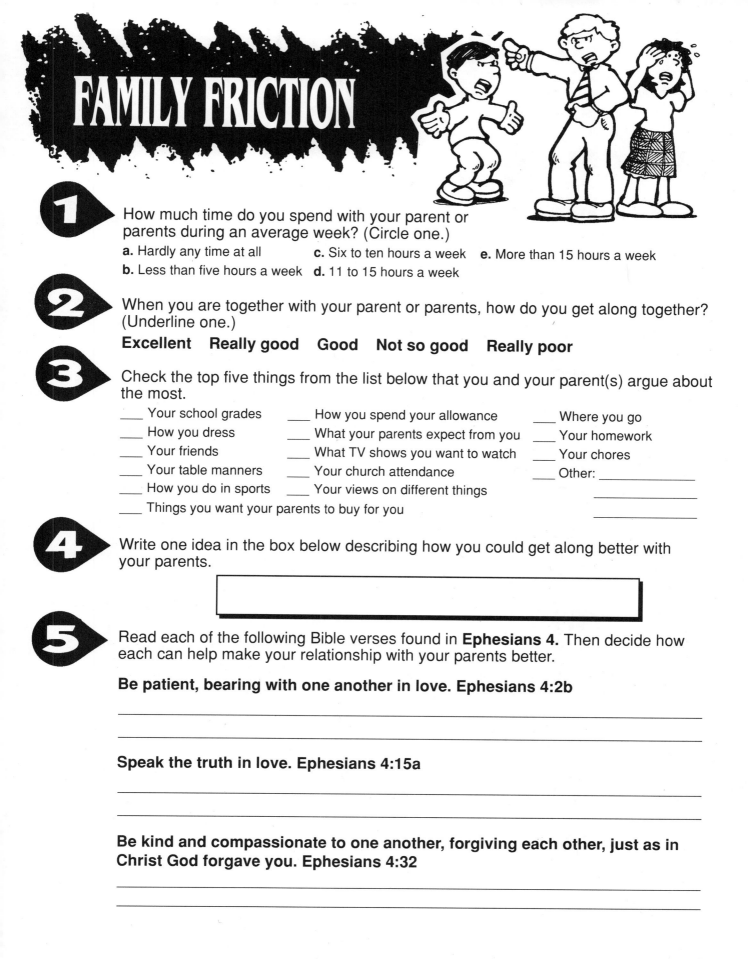

1 How much time do you spend with your parent or parents during an average week? (Circle one.)

a. Hardly any time at all   **c.** Six to ten hours a week   **e.** More than 15 hours a week

b. Less than five hours a week   **d.** 11 to 15 hours a week

2 When you are together with your parent or parents, how do you get along together? (Underline one.)

Excellent   **Really good**   **Good**   **Not so good**   **Really poor**

3 Check the top five things from the list below that you and your parent(s) argue about the most.

___ Your school grades   ___ How you spend your allowance   ___ Where you go

___ How you dress   ___ What your parents expect from you   ___ Your homework

___ Your friends   ___ What TV shows you want to watch   ___ Your chores

___ Your table manners   ___ Your church attendance   ___ Other: _____

___ How you do in sports   ___ Your views on different things   _____

___ Things you want your parents to buy for you   _____

4 Write one idea in the box below describing how you could get along better with your parents.

5 Read each of the following Bible verses found in **Ephesians 4.** Then decide how each can help make your relationship with your parents better.

Be patient, bearing with one another in love. Ephesians 4:2b

_____

_____

Speak the truth in love. Ephesians 4:15a

_____

_____

Be kind and compassionate to one another, forgiving each other, just as in Christ God forgave you. Ephesians 4:32

_____

_____

Date Used: _____

Group: _____

FAMILY FRICTION
Topic: Getting Along With Parents

Purpose of this Session:

As kids get older, getting along gets tougher. You used to hear the complaint from young people in high school and junior high, "My folks don't understand." Now this is heard from kids in the upper elementary grades. Use this TalkSheet to discuss how young people can better get along with their parents, stepparents, or adult guardians.

To Introduce the Topic:

Ask your group members to place their two hands together, palms flat. Have them slowly move their hands up and down. As they are doing this, explain that one hand represents their parents and the other themselves. When they were younger, there wasn't much friction between them. But as they have grown up, they want to move one way and their parents want them to move another. Ask them now to speed up the movement of their hands.

   Explain that there will be times when this friction in their families will heat up, just as they can feel the heat caused by the friction of their hand motions. But this heat does not have to get red hot. There are things kids (and parents, too!) can do to keep things cool.

The Discussion:

Item #1: Ask what the ideal together time would be if kids had their choice. During this discussion you will want to listen to the young people while at the same time support the role parents play and the difficulties parents face in raising children.

Item #2: Explore with the kids the role they play in getting along with their parents. Tell the group that families are different. Some do better at different things. Some are strained by a parental job loss, a divorce, or child abuse. Brainstorm with the group how kids who lack a supportive home can find needed support in constructive ways (as opposed to destructive ways, such as acting out in school, smoking, or gang involvement).

Item #3: Address each of these issues with sensitivity. Have volunteers role-play how they can better get along. You can set up situations from stories the kids provide from their top-five lists.

   Create a group list to see what the kids chose as the top five. Point out how family friction is part of growing up and that they do have some control in minimizing it. Be careful not to blame either parents or kids for the family friction. Your goal is to empower the kids to positively change their family relationships with the help of the Spirit of God working in their lives.

Item #4: Create a large list of statements from the ideas provided by the group. Ask the students to identify those at the top of the list. Then have the kids describe how they could put these into practice in their home lives.

Item #5: Ask how practical each of these biblical principles is in terms of family life.

To Close the Session:

Close by creating a list with the group of all the practical and positive benefits that kids get out of working on their relationships with their parents. The group can also brainstorm and plan an event with parents that would help the parents and kids better understand and communicate with each other.

JUST AS IF I NEVER SINNED

1 Place a check mark in front of each of the following that you think are examples of sin.

_____ Cheating on a spelling test _____ Shoplifting a candy bar
_____ Yelling at your mom _____ Not doing your homework
_____ Watching TV _____ Copying a friend's homework
_____ Forgetting to do your chores _____ Listening to rock music
_____ Gossiping about a friend _____ Lying to a teacher
_____ Arguing with your dad _____ Calling someone a name

2 Go back to Item #1 and put an X in front of each of the things you think are really big sins.

3 Write out below your definition of *sin*.

_____

_____

4 Decide if you **AGREE** or **DISAGREE** with each of the following statements.

a. Sin can bring a kid closer to God. ___ **I AGREE** ___ **I DISAGREE**
b. God is only sad about big sins. ___ **I AGREE** ___ **I DISAGREE**
c. There are some sins that God will not forgive. ___ **I AGREE** ___ **I DISAGREE**
d. There is a difference between kid sins
   and adult sins. ___ **I AGREE** ___ **I DISAGREE**
e. Doing good things gets you closer to God. ___ **I AGREE** ___ **I DISAGREE**

5 *Justification* is a Bible doctrine. A doctrine is a statement that describes what the Bible is teaching us. Justification means that God has chosen to look at us as though we never sinned. It is like God took a huge eraser and wiped out all our sins.

Why do you need to be justified? _____

_____

_____

6 Read one of the Scripture passages below that talk about the Bible doctrine being studied in this TalkSheet.
Romans 3:20–26 Romans 4:20–25 Galatians 2:15, 16

JUST AS IF I NEVER SINNED
Topic: Justification

Purpose of this Session:

Many kids are unaware of the basic Bible doctrines. In fact, many are unaware of what a doctrine is. Kids rarely have the opportunity to talk with adults and with each other about the important beliefs in Christianity. They are confused about the work of Christ on our behalf. Use this TalkSheet to discuss one of the important doctrines of the Christian faith.

To Introduce the Topic:

Make a list of all the words kids can think of that describe sin. Write each of these words down for everyone to see. The following are some examples of words your group may consider:

Error	Backslide	Evil	Wickedness	Mistake
Vice	Blooper	Blunder	Screwup	Wrongdoing
Scandal	Delinquent	Corruption	Naughty	Criminal

Some kids may need more help and prompting than others. Do not have the group list actual sins, only substitute words for sin. The kids will get very creative in their thinking—some will even make up words.

The Discussion:

Item #1: This activity helps kids see that they are sinners. It is easy for kids to feel that sin is not a problem for them since they have not done anything really bad. The point of this activity is not to berate young people but to help them recognize their sinfulness.

Item #2: Point out that God does not look at the size of our sins. Many kids, and even adults, think that as long as they don't commit really "big" sins, they are okay before God. But any sin disqualifies us from a relationship with God. God's standard is sinlessness. People recognize differences in sin because some sins have more adverse consequences than others.

Item #3: The biblical view of sin is missing the mark. Anytime we miss God's standard, we have sinned.

Item #4: Clarify any misconceptions that kids have about God and sin. Some kids feel that there are some sins that God will never forgive. Point out that Christ did not go to the cross for only certain types of sins. Spend additional time discussing the statement "Doing good things gets you closer to God." There is nothing that we can do to earn favor with God.

Item #5: Explain to the group that God can justify sinners because Christ died on the cross for those sins. Paul taught in Romans that it is through faith in Jesus that Christians are justified. This does not mean that salvation is worked for or earned. Faith is not the grounds of justification. There is nothing that can be done to earn justification by God. Genesis 15:6 states that God looked at Abraham's faith and "credited it to him as righteousness." Abraham did not work for that righteousness. God looked at him and treated him "just as if he had never sinned."

Ask the kids if someone has ever done something for them that they did not deserve. This illustrates God's unmerited favor toward the Christian. When God justifies a believer, it has nothing to do with what the believer does. No one can do enough good things to win God's grace. We have nothing and God has everything to do with our justification.

Item #6: Choose a passage to study with your group.

To Close the Session:

Summarize what has been covered during the discussion. You can effectively illustrate justification by using the example of a courtroom scene much like the TV courtroom shows that are popular. Point out that we are guilty of sinning. The prosecuting attorney can easily prove that we are guilty. The penalty for our sin is death and eternal damnation. However, Christ as our defense attorney goes before God, the judge, and argues our case. Since he died on the cross for our sins, he can demonstrate our innocence. God can now treat us as if we had never sinned. Review the fact that all of us need forgiveness for our sins no matter how small we think those sins are. Invite the group to pray a prayer of faith asking that God justify them.

GROWIN' UP IN CHURCH

1 Fill in the blank in the sentence below with the word *more* or the word *less*.
I wish kids my age had _____ things to do at church.

2 In the rectangle below, write down your favorite church activity.

3 Answer **YES** or **NO** to each of the following statements.
a. A kid should attend church every week. __ YES __ NO
b. A parent should make a kid attend church. __ YES __ NO
c. Church is usually boring. __ YES __ NO
d. I feel I learn many new things at church. __ YES __ NO
e. Church is one of the most important things in my life. __ YES __ NO

4 Complete the following sentence: **One thing I would like to see my church do differently with kids is . . .** _____

_____

5 What would you lose if you were told you could never attend church again? _____

_____

_____

6 Read the following scrambled verse found in **Luke 4:16** by using the numbers, beginning with #1. Do you feel Christ liked or disliked church attendance and participation as much as you?

    4. as was his custom.
    3. and on the Sabbath day he went into the synagogue,
    1. He went to Nazareth,
    5. And he stood up to read.
    2. where he had been brought up,

Date Used: _____

Group: _____

GROWIN' UP IN CHURCH
Topic: Church Participation

Purpose of this Session:
Church or some form of religious instruction is a part of life for the majority of American 4th–6th graders. Most kids report that religion is an important influence in their lives. Use this TalkSheet to support the role church can play in the lives of young people as well as a tool for getting ideas on how your church can improve on its work with kids.

To Introduce the Topic:
Draw a simple outline of a church on a chalkboard or on newsprint. Make it large enough to write inside. Ask your students to call out words that come to their minds when they think of the word church.

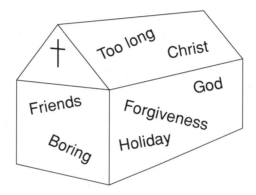

The Discussion:
Item #1: You will hear grumbling from some kids that they are made to go to church. Don't discount these complaints but listen to them as real. You may want to take some time to explore this with the group if it appears to be a major issue. Keep the discussion positive, supportive of parents, and validating for the young people—no easy task. Ask what other things kids have to do. Explore why parents might see church as important for kids.

Item #2: Ask the kids why these are favorites. This activity can indicate what your church is doing right and how it can be strengthened. Create a master list of all the favorites to see if a pattern can be identified.

Item #3: You will need to define what you mean by church here. Usually kids see it as the worship service and Sunday school. Ask the group to react to each statement, then spend time on those that stir up controversy or discussion.

Item #4: Take these suggestions seriously and you will find that kids will take ownership to plan and carry them out. Some great ideas will come out of this activity.

Item #5: Focus on how kids' lives might change. Some young people may interpret this with a focus on weekly attendance. Place the focus on the relationships, values, and spiritual growth that may be lost rather than just attendance loss. Create with the group a master list of all the benefits of church involvement.

Item #6: Ask why Jesus went to the synagogue regularly. Read Hebrews 10:25, and ask why the author of this passage wants Christians to encourage each other's participation in church.

To Close the Session:
Close the session by returning to the introductory activity. Draw another church, and ask the kids to fill it with words that describe how they would like to see church. Brainstorm ways your group members could make this new description a reality.

End on a very positive note by asking volunteers to share the most important things they have learned in the last year from their involvement in church.

TWO-WAY TALK

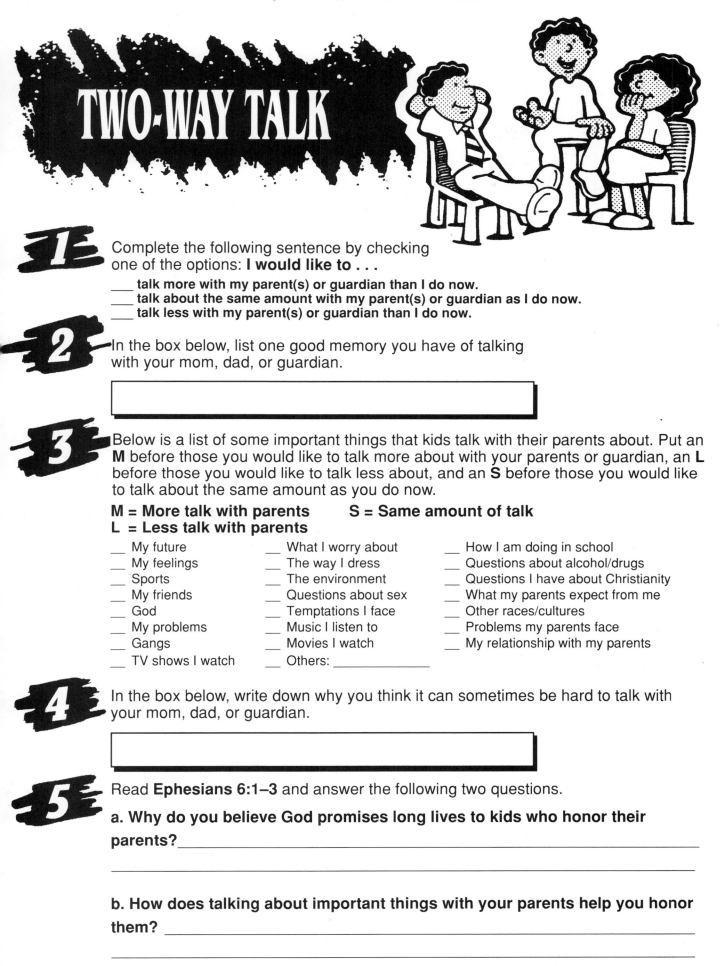

1 Complete the following sentence by checking one of the options: **I would like to . . .**

___ talk more with my parent(s) or guardian than I do now.
___ talk about the same amount with my parent(s) or guardian as I do now.
___ talk less with my parent(s) or guardian than I do now.

2 In the box below, list one good memory you have of talking with your mom, dad, or guardian.

>

3 Below is a list of some important things that kids talk with their parents about. Put an **M** before those you would like to talk more about with your parents or guardian, an **L** before those you would like to talk less about, and an **S** before those you would like to talk about the same amount as you do now.

M = More talk with parents   S = Same amount of talk
L = Less talk with parents

__ My future	__ What I worry about	__ How I am doing in school
__ My feelings	__ The way I dress	__ Questions about alcohol/drugs
__ Sports	__ The environment	__ Questions I have about Christianity
__ My friends	__ Questions about sex	__ What my parents expect from me
__ God	__ Temptations I face	__ Other races/cultures
__ My problems	__ Music I listen to	__ Problems my parents face
__ Gangs	__ Movies I watch	__ My relationship with my parents
__ TV shows I watch	__ Others: _____	

4 In the box below, write down why you think it can sometimes be hard to talk with your mom, dad, or guardian.

>

5 Read **Ephesians 6:1–3** and answer the following two questions.

a. Why do you believe God promises long lives to kids who honor their parents?_____

_____

b. How does talking about important things with your parents help you honor them? _____

_____

Date Used: _____

Group: _____

TWO-WAY TALK
Topic: Parent/Child Communication

Purpose of this Session:

It's trite, but true—communication is the key. It's no secret that without healthy communication, family life becomes strained. Children and youth workers are in an ideal position to support and encourage family communication. Take this time to reinforce the all-important, parent-kid talk that makes families work.

To Introduce the Topic:

For many kids, the traditional family is only a reality on *Leave It to Beaver* television reruns. This introductory activity gives you a group picture of the makeup of your kids' families. Ask the students to help you create a list of all the adults who are parents with whom they live or visit. Below is a sample of a typical list. Write the list on a chalkboard or on newsprint for everyone to see.

Birth mother	Birth father
Big brother	Big sister
Grandmother	Grandfather
Stepmother	Stepfather
Parent's boyfriend	Parent's girlfriend
Guardian	Foster parent

The Discussion:

Item #1: Today's kids don't have as many opportunities to talk with their parents as past generations had, but many kids report that they want more communication. Explore with the kids why they responded the way they did.

Item #2: Let the students share their memories and explain why they remember them as good. Ask how they can make these memories happen again.

Item #3: Briefly discuss each of these issues. Answer the question, "Why is this an important issue that needs to be discussed with a parent?" Examine why kids want some of these issues to be discussed less. For example, during a discussion using this TalkSheet, a fifth grader reported he wanted to talk more about his problems and less about his mother's. His mother had been divorced twice and was at the time living with her boyfriend and her son. According to this young man, she was dumping her problems on him. There was a role reversal in this family. This boy was able to get support and encouragement through the TalkSheet discussion.

Item #4: Support the kids as they share the struggles and frustrations they have experienced talking with their parents. Ask the group to offer suggestions to the problems kids report.

Item #5: Read aloud Ephesians 6:4a. This command to fathers emphasizes that family communication is a two-way street. Explain that kids have control over their part of that two-way communication. Encourage them to do their part.

To Close the Session:

Have the kids form a circle. One at a time, ask the kids to commit to the group to go home and talk with their parents about one of the issues from Item #3. Have volunteers role-play how they might do this. The kids can use your discussion time as an excuse to bring up the subject with their parents. They might tell their parents that they have an assignment to talk with them about the future, God, questions about sex, or whatever topic they choose. The group members can help each other think of questions to ask their parents to get the conversation going. At your next meeting, kids can report on their conversations with their parents.

WORLD KIDS

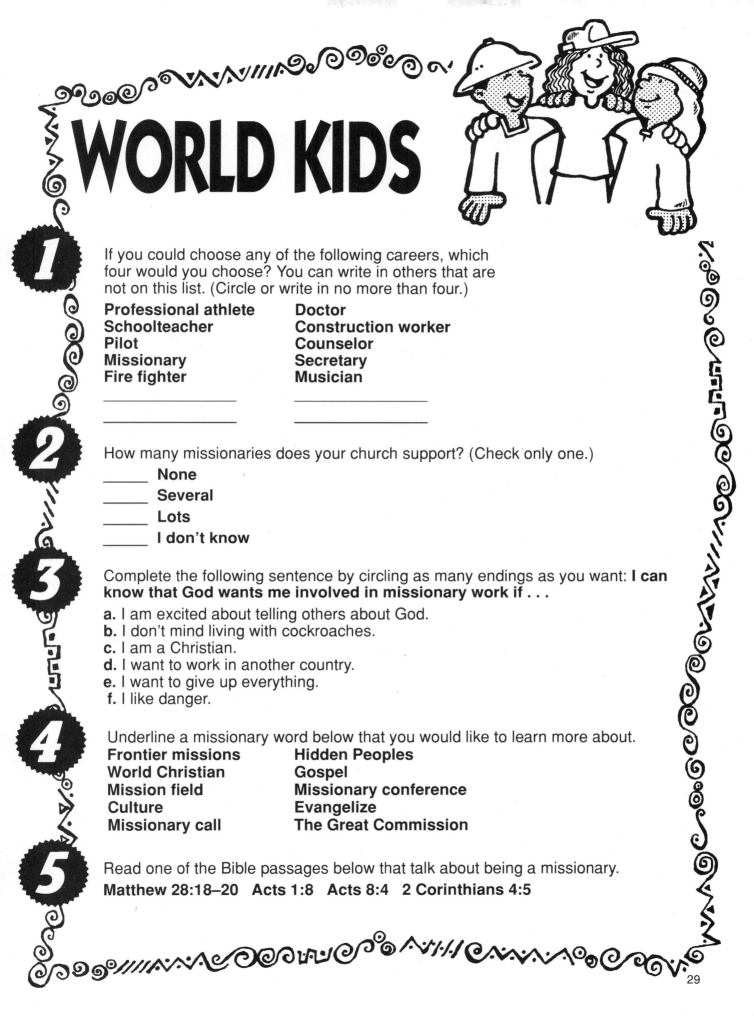

1 If you could choose any of the following careers, which four would you choose? You can write in others that are not on this list. (Circle or write in no more than four.)

Professional athlete　　**Doctor**
Schoolteacher　　　　　**Construction worker**
Pilot　　　　　　　　　**Counselor**
Missionary　　　　　　 **Secretary**
Fire fighter　　　　　　 **Musician**

_____　　　_____

_____　　　_____

2 How many missionaries does your church support? (Check only one.)

_____ **None**

_____ **Several**

_____ **Lots**

_____ **I don't know**

3 Complete the following sentence by circling as many endings as you want: **I can know that God wants me involved in missionary work if . . .**

a. I am excited about telling others about God.
b. I don't mind living with cockroaches.
c. I am a Christian.
d. I want to work in another country.
e. I want to give up everything.
f. I like danger.

4 Underline a missionary word below that you would like to learn more about.

Frontier missions　　**Hidden Peoples**
World Christian　　　**Gospel**
Mission field　　　　 **Missionary conference**
Culture　　　　　　　**Evangelize**
Missionary call　　　 **The Great Commission**

5 Read one of the Bible passages below that talk about being a missionary.
Matthew 28:18–20　Acts 1:8　Acts 8:4　2 Corinthians 4:5

Date Used: _____

Group: _____

WORLD KIDS
Topic: Missionary Work

Purpose of this Session:

The title of this TalkSheet is taken from the concept of the World Christian. David Bryant says, "World Christians are day-to-day disciples for whom Christ's global cause has become the integrating, overriding priority for all that He is for them."* Young people can never catch a vision for Christ's global cause if they are never introduced to what God is doing in the world and how they can be a part of transforming it for Christ. This TalkSheet introduces kids to global missionary work.

To Introduce the Topic:

If you have access to a globe or a map of the world and a magnifying glass, ask your kids to take a closer look at the world. Different young people can name specific regions and cities they see through the magnifying glass. If you don't have a map, a globe, or a magnifying glass, have the kids list all the different places they are familiar with around the world, and write them on a chalkboard or on newsprint. Then talk with your young people about the kids who live in these faraway places. What concerns do they have? Do they worry about the same things kids in our country worry about? Do they have similar problems? What might it be like to be a kid in another country? Then tell the group that you are going to talk about the world, God's plan for it, and how each and every young person in attendance fits into that plan.

The Discussion:

Item #1: Kids will see by this activity that the work of a missionary is a career choice available to them as Christians. Too often, we don't talk with kids about this as a career option. Missionary work is no holier than other professions. Kids need to know that we need Christian fire fighters, lawyers, and sales clerks. But the church also needs to send out missionaries. Explore with the group some of the positions missionaries hold as they share the Gospel—nurses, doctors, writers, printers, pastors, engineers, schoolteachers, secretaries, and more.

Item #2: Ask the kids if they believe missionary work is still needed. You can explain that a missionary is someone who goes to another culture and tells people about God's forgiveness through Jesus Christ. Bring some information you can share with your group about the missionaries your church supports and why. Answer any questions the group may have about these missionaries.

Item #3: Point out that God wants all Christians involved in missionary work. Make a list with the group of the things the kids can do to get involved.

Item #4: You will need to do some personal research or ask someone familiar with these and other terms to talk with your group. A good starting point is the book listed below.

Item #5: Explain that missionary work was the emphasis of the early church because it is the center of God's plan for the world.

To Close the Session:

Write individual letters or a group letter to the missionaries your church supports asking the questions the young people have raised during your discussion. When they are returned, discuss the responses with your group. Close by reading John 3:16–21.

*David Bryant, *In the Gap: What It Means to Be a World Christian* (Downers Grove, Ill.: InterVarsity Christian Fellowship, 1979), 63.

BEING A KID IN A GROWN-UP'S WORLD

1 What are the two best and the two worst things about being a kid?

BEST THINGS	WORST THINGS
a. _____	**a.** _____
b. _____	**b.** _____

2 Respond to each of the following statements by placing an **X** before either **YES** or **NO.**

a. Grown-ups are more important than kids. ___ **YES** ___ **NO**
b. Grown-ups do not understand kids. ___ **YES** ___ **NO**
c. Kids can do things that grown-ups cannot. ___ **YES** ___ **NO**
d. Grown-ups decide too many things for kids. ___ **YES** ___ **NO**

3 What will you not do or say to kids when you are a grown-up? (Check your top five choices.)

___ Swear at kids
___ Yell at kids
___ Tease kids
___ Embarrass kids
___ Spank kids
___ Be too busy for kids

___ Be rude to kids
___ Boss kids around
___ Make kids do things they don't want to do
___ Get mad at kids about little things
___ Take things away from kids
___ Say to kids that adults know more than kids

4 Do you think it is easier being a grown-up or easier being a kid?

___ **It is easier being a grown-up.**
___ **It is easier being a kid.**

Why? _____

5 Why do you believe God puts grown-ups in your life?

_____
_____

6 Read one of the following Bible passages, then write down three things you feel kids can do as a ministry.

2 Chronicles 34:1–2, 31   Samuel 2:18   John 6:9

a. _____
b. _____
c. _____

Date Used: _____

Group: _____

BEING A KID IN A GROWN-UP'S WORLD
Topic: Childhood

Purpose of this Session:

Being a kid can be frustrating, especially in a world designed for adults. Young people need the opportunity to share what it is like for them in a grown-up's world. Too often, kidhood is seen as prep time for adulthood, and young people are rushed through childhood. But it is okay to be a kid! This TalkSheet structures a discussion that supports kids in being kids.

To Introduce the Topic:

A good lead-in to the discussion is to ask the kids to share their parents' when-I-was-your-age stories. The young people will have an enjoyable time sharing "adult" stories about growing up. Tell the group that you will be discussing being a kid in a world of adults.

The Discussion:

Item #1: First, kids will mention things they do not have to do, such as pay bills, go to work, or do laundry. Then they will identify things they cannot do, such as drive, watch certain movies, or go to bed anytime they wish. Kids may mention some painful situations, like dealing with divorce. Keep the group a safe place where kids can share their difficult situations.

Item #2: The statement "Grown-ups are more important than kids" helps young people articulate their feelings of insignificance in an adult world. The statement "Kids can do things that grown-ups cannot" focuses on why kids are as important as adults. Explore how God can work through kids. Many kids have not considered what they can do for God.

Students typically agree with the statement "Grown-ups do not understand kids." As an adult, listen to why kids agree with this. Kids feel that adults today do not understand what is happening in their world. They feel grown-ups do not take the time to listen to them. You probably felt the same way when you were their age.

The statement "Kids can do things that grown-ups cannot" provides the opportunity to examine kidhood in general. Too often, adults view kids as adults in training. Kids have to do this and learn that to become adults. Preparing for adulthood is only one of the tasks of childhood.

Young people can have a kid relationship with God, great friendships, and even ministries. By getting good at being kids, young people are preparing for adulthood.

The statement "Grown-ups decide too many things for kids" will be met with enthusiastic agreement. Explore with your students the things that are under their control and the things that adults control. Then discuss how they can make better decisions regarding the things under their control.

Item #3: Remember that list you created in your head of all the things you said you would never do to kids when you became an adult? Think back on it so you can be empathetic with the kids as they share those things that parents and other adults say and do that they do not like. Encourage the kids to ask their parents if there was anything they said they would not do to kids when they grew up.

Item #4: Interestingly, many kids believe they will handle adulthood better than they have kidhood. They feel that once they are out on their own, they will make better decisions. Explore with the kids how getting good at being a kid will help them in adulthood. If they can make good decisions now, they will make good decisions as grown-ups.

Item #5: Create a list of roles adults play in the lives of kids: protector, guide, teacher, listener, comforter, and so on. Point out that adults make mistakes just like kids do.

Item #6: Each of the Scriptures speaks of a ministry young people had in Bible times. Read the passages, then discuss ministry opportunities kids can involve themselves in today.

To Close the Session:

Review what has been discussed. Use this time to let the adults in the group encourage and build up your kids. Adults can share how well they feel the kids are doing at being kids.

PRAYER POWER

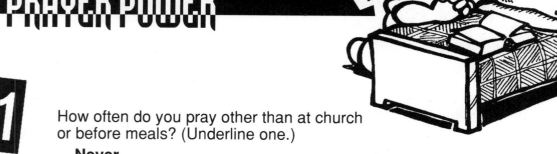

1 How often do you pray other than at church or before meals? (Underline one.)

Never

Rarely

Once a month

Once a week

Several times in a week

Once a day

Several times in a day

2 Complete the following sentence: **Usually I pray when . . .** _____

_____

_____

3 The prayers of adults are more important to God than the prayers of kids.

___ **True**   ___ **False**

4 How is prayer like talking with a friend on the phone?

_____

_____

_____

5 Rearrange the following words found in **1 Chronicles 16:11** so that they make sense.

to strength; the Lord and seek his face Look his always.

_____

_____

Date used:_____

Group: _____

PRAYER POWER
Topic: Prayer

Purpose of this Session:
Young people at this age are becoming more aware of their prayer lives. Unfortunately, for many of them, prayer becomes a chore as they grow older. But prayer need not be something they have to do or only do when they are in trouble. Prayer is God's invitation to have a relationship with him. Take this TalkSheet opportunity to expand your kids' views on prayer.

To Introduce the Topic:
Ask the kids to describe how they prayed when they were much younger. Then ask them to describe how they pray differently today. Their views on prayer, at least for many of the kids, will have changed. When they were younger they asked for stuff (which they still do as older kids), but they have broadened their views of God and talking with him. He is becoming more of a friend. Kids will also mention that when they were younger they thought the position they prayed in was really important, that their prayers were really simple, that their prayers are now more complicated, or that now they talk more with God.

The Discussion:
Item #1: Obtain a group consensus on the number of times the kids pray. Ask how much of this is "have to" and how much is "want to."

Item #2: Ask the kids to share their answers while you create a list of the responses. The focus, aside from before meals or at bedtime, is often on things like, "I'm in a tight spot," "I know someone who is sick," "I've had a bad day," "I'm worried," "I feel down," "something bad has happened," and so on. Kids have gotten a distorted view of God with these perceptions of prayer. Create another list that focuses on developing a relationship with God through prayer of which needing help is only one slice of that friendship.

Item #3: Most young people know and will say that the prayers of adults are not more important than those of kids, but they often feel that adults discount their prayers. One girl responded, "Kids have just as many problems as adults, and God listens when kids tell him about these problems." Use this opportunity to validate the importance of the prayers of kids.

Item #4: Create a list with the kids of all the things they talk about on the phone with their friends. Then create a list of all the things they talk with God about in prayer. Compare the list and discuss how prayer is like talking with their friend, God. Ask why people have so much difficulty talking regularly with God as a friend.

Item #5: 1 Chronicles 16:11 says, "Look to the Lord and his strength; seek his face always." Other good prayer passages to discuss are Matthew 6:7–13 and Hebrews 4:15, 16. Stress that we can talk with God anytime, anywhere, about anything.

To Close the Session:
Close by spending group time in prayer. Ask each group member to think of one word he or she could say to God in a one-word prayer. Give examples like love or thanks or help. With the group sitting in a circle (break large groups into smaller ones), have one young person begin and move around the circle. Close with your own word and "amen." Let the group make some observations about what occurred. Often the focus is on mechanics. Did we hold hands correctly or say the right words? Try this same one-word group prayer again. This time you will find the group relaxing and getting more genuinely involved in the prayer. Again, make some observations about what happened.

You may now want to spend additional time in prayer after creating a group prayer list that all the kids can see as they volunteer to pray.

FRIEND FACTOR

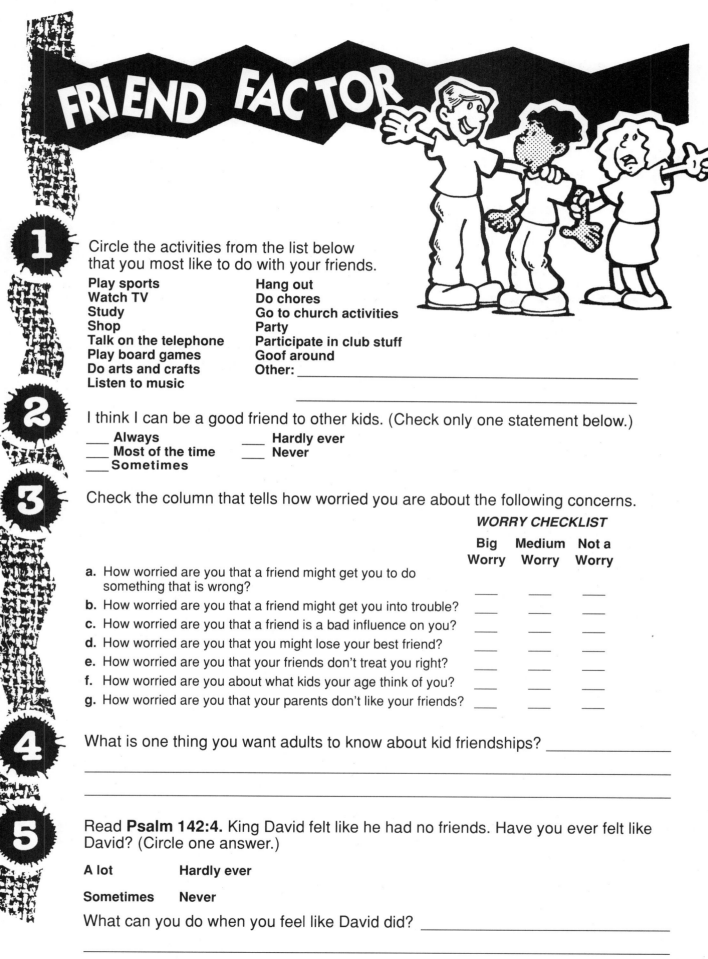

1 Circle the activities from the list below that you most like to do with your friends.

Play sports   **Hang out**
Watch TV   **Do chores**
Study   **Go to church activities**
Shop   **Party**
Talk on the telephone **Participate in club stuff**
Play board games   **Goof around**
Do arts and crafts   **Other:** _____
Listen to music   _____

2 I think I can be a good friend to other kids. (Check only one statement below.)

___ **Always**   ___ **Hardly ever**
___ **Most of the time** ___ **Never**
___ **Sometimes**

3 Check the column that tells how worried you are about the following concerns.

WORRY CHECKLIST

	Big Worry	Medium Worry	Not a Worry
a. How worried are you that a friend might get you to do something that is wrong?	___	___	___
b. How worried are you that a friend might get you into trouble?	___	___	___
c. How worried are you that a friend is a bad influence on you?	___	___	___
d. How worried are you that you might lose your best friend?	___	___	___
e. How worried are you that your friends don't treat you right?	___	___	___
f. How worried are you about what kids your age think of you?	___	___	___
g. How worried are you that your parents don't like your friends?	___	___	___

4 What is one thing you want adults to know about kid friendships? _____

_____

_____

5 Read **Psalm 142:4.** King David felt like he had no friends. Have you ever felt like David? (Circle one answer.)

A lot   **Hardly ever**

Sometimes **Never**

What can you do when you feel like David did? _____

_____

Date Used: _____

Group: _____

FRIEND FACTOR
Topic: Friendship

Purpose of this Session:

Friendships become increasingly important as kids enter the upper elementary grades, and parents become increasingly concerned about their kids' friendship choices. Making and keeping friends can be tough. Our mobile society means friends come and go, so young people are nearly always establishing new friendships. Use this TalkSheet to discuss the importance of friendships and good friendship choices.

To Introduce the Topic:

Have a young person who is wearing pants lay down on a large piece of newsprint. Draw his or her outline with a washable marker. Take care not to mark the person's clothes. Tape the finished outline to a wall. Tell the kids that they are going to create the "perfect" friend. As they call out words that describe their idea of the perfect friend, write these words inside the outline of the body. You can refer back to this list throughout your discussion.

The Discussion:

Item #1: This gives you an idea of all the things your kids do with their friends. Make a master list of the top five activities. Don't allow the young people to put down anyone's activities. For example, if a girl adds that she likes to play dress up and a group pokes fun at this, take the time to talk this through. Negative feedback of this sort only serves to hurt friendships. Point out to the group that this TalkSheet discussion can be a time to support each other in building good friendships.

Item #2: Refer back to your introductory activity. Kids will say they don't want to be friends with some kids, which is appropriate. Some kids are mean, antisocial, do drugs, and so on. But some kids are simply overweight or unpopular. Ask your group members how they can be friendly without having to be best friends with everyone.

Item #3: Parents are not the only ones who are concerned about negative peer influence; young people report many friendship worries, too. Adults can't control the friendship choices and battles kids face, but they can listen and acknowledge the concerns kids express and help them problem solve their way through them. Discuss each of these statements and help the young people get a new perspective on their friendship concerns by sharing their thoughts and feelings with the different group members—youths and adults.

The question "How worried are you that your parents don't like your friends?" needs extra discussion time. Problem solve with the kids, but be sure to support the concern parents have. Explore with the kids why parents might be so concerned about their friends.

Create two headings on a chalkboard or on newsprint: **How Friends Influence Us** and **How We Influence Friends.** Brainstorm a list of ideas under each of the headings.

Item #4: Kids have a lot to say to adults about friendships, much of which applies to adult friendships as well. Brainstorm ways kids can communicate these feelings in constructive ways to their parents and other adults, like teachers.

Item #5: David did have friends (1 Samuel 18:1–3; 2 Samuel 15:37), but at that moment in his life, David felt alone. David's answer was to turn to the Lord. Examine how your kids can also turn to the Lord with their friendship concerns.

To Close the Session:

Summarize the different points that have been made during the discussion. Close the session by asking the kids to list all the ways that God can be their friend.

REPORT CARD FOR MY SCHOOL

1 If you could be principal for a day at your school, what is one change you would make? _____

_____

_____

2 Circle the grade you would give your school. **A+** is the best and **F** is failing.

A+	B+	C+	D+	
A	B	C	D	F
A-	B-	C-	D-	

3 Put a check beside the five biggest concerns you have at school.

___ Talking out of turn
___ Being teased
___ Getting hit
___ Daydreaming
___ Being embarrassed
___ Feeling like I don't belong
___ Difficult tests
___ Being bored
___ Not having enough books
___ Not being liked by kids
___ Losing a friend
___ Not having enough homework
___ Being harassed by gangs
___ Eating food that's not good
___ Getting another new kid in class

___ Being treated cruelly by other kids
___ Not having enough friends
___ Having rumors spread about me by other kids
___ Mean teachers
___ Getting pressured to do things that are wrong
___ Not getting good enough grades
___ Changing schools
___ Class work that's too hard
___ Not being part of the popular group
___ Getting called bad names
___ Having problems on the school bus
___ Not understanding the teacher
___ Too much homework
___ Other: _____
  _____

4 It is easy to be a Christian at my school.
  _____ **True**   _____ **False**

5 When you have a problem at school, whom do you normally talk to?

_____ My teacher
_____ A friend
_____ The principal
_____ God

_____ An adult at school other than my teacher
_____ My mom, dad, stepparent, or guardian
_____ An adult at church
_____ No one

6 Read the following scrambled verse found in Proverbs 3:5–7.

6. **Do not be wise in your own eyes;**
2. **with all your heart**
7. **fear the LORD and shun evil.**
1. **Trust in the LORD**
5. **and he will make your paths straight.**
4. **in all your ways acknowledge him,**
3. **and lean not on your own understanding;**

Date Used: _____

Group: _____

REPORT CARD FOR MY SCHOOL
Topic: School Life

Purpose of this Session:
Kids are required by law to attend school. Adults and kids will tell you that schooling is important. Yet for many kids, the joy and excitement they felt when they began school in kindergarten diminishes each year they attend. By the upper elementary school years, students not only lose interest in their course work, they also perceive their teachers as being less caring than in earlier grades. Much of the concern and disinterest kids express about school is due to their inability to change their circumstances. They feel powerless to control a large chunk of their day. Give your students the opportunity to talk with each other and with adults about their school experiences. Use this TalkSheet as an opportunity to listen and to create an environment where your kids can feel God's grace extended to their school life.

To Introduce the Topic:
Ask four volunteer young people who represent two different schools to come to the front of the group. Seat each of them in a chair with the students from opposing schools facing each other. Tell them they are going to participate in a school competition. They each have 30 seconds to say as many positive things about their schools as they can. The group can vote on which school received the most compliments. The school with the highest number of positive statements wins.

The Discussion:
Item #1: List each of the suggested changes on a chalkboard or on newsprint. Ask the group why these changes are necessary.

Item #2: The same school might get an A+ and an F from different students, depending upon their experiences. Let the group members share their grades and their reasoning.

Item #3: Create a master list of the concerns checked by the students. Narrow these down to the five biggest concerns.

Item #4: Ask the students what it means to be a Christian at their schools and how Christ could make a difference there. You will find that many students have never thought about this issue before.

Item #5: All students need someone to talk with about their school frustrations. Assure kids that they can talk with you. Point out that keeping problems to themselves is not a solution to their problems. Even if a talk can't solve their problems, they will feel better knowing that someone else knows, cares, and appreciates what they are feeling.

Item #6: This passage encourages us to commit the school day and every day to God. Just as adults worry about their daily tasks at work, young people worry about their school day. Will I do this worksheet correctly? I need to look at my spelling list before the test! Why won't Brad play with me? Explore with the kids how they can trust and acknowledge God during their school day.

To Close the Session:
Close the session by asking the kids to identify the different parts of school. They might mention athletics, social activities, schoolwork, and homework. Place the headings they give you on a chalkboard or on newsprint. Under each heading have the young people identify a series of problems that kids face in that aspect of school. Then engage the group in a problem-solving session around these identified issues. Challenge the group members to see themselves as a Christian community that is solving these problems together.

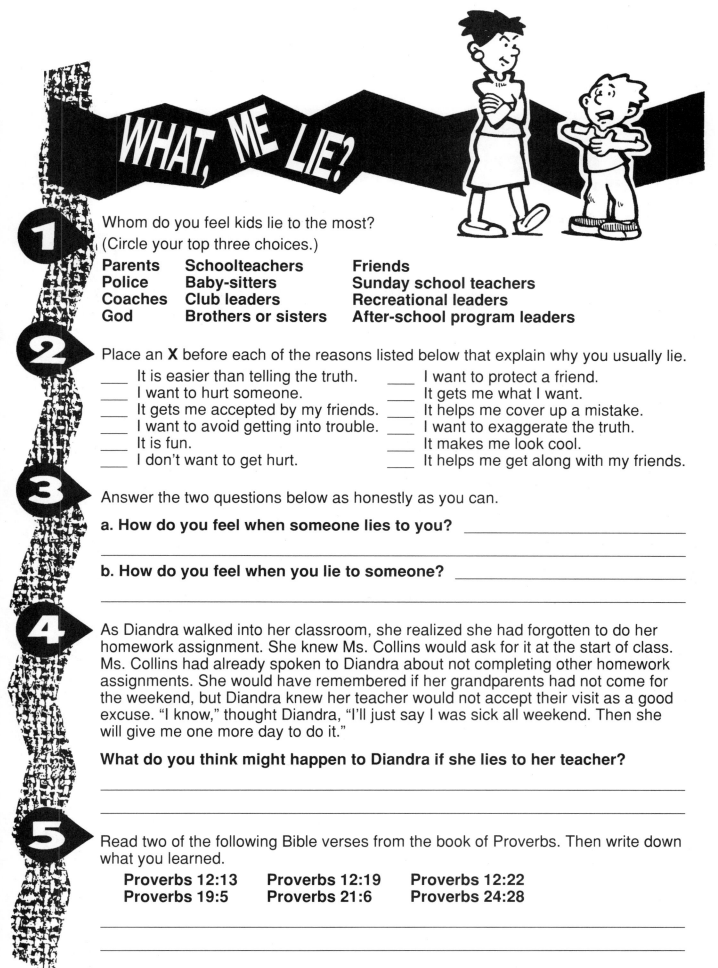

WHAT, ME LIE?

1 Whom do you feel kids lie to the most?
(Circle your top three choices.)

Parents	**Schoolteachers**	**Friends**
Police	**Baby-sitters**	**Sunday school teachers**
Coaches	**Club leaders**	**Recreational leaders**
God	**Brothers or sisters**	**After-school program leaders**

2 Place an **X** before each of the reasons listed below that explain why you usually lie.

____ It is easier than telling the truth.   ____ I want to protect a friend.
____ I want to hurt someone.   ____ It gets me what I want.
____ It gets me accepted by my friends.   ____ It helps me cover up a mistake.
____ I want to avoid getting into trouble.   ____ I want to exaggerate the truth.
____ It is fun.   ____ It makes me look cool.
____ I don't want to get hurt.   ____ It helps me get along with my friends.

3 Answer the two questions below as honestly as you can.

a. How do you feel when someone lies to you? _____

_____

b. How do you feel when you lie to someone? _____

_____

4 As Diandra walked into her classroom, she realized she had forgotten to do her homework assignment. She knew Ms. Collins would ask for it at the start of class. Ms. Collins had already spoken to Diandra about not completing other homework assignments. She would have remembered if her grandparents had not come for the weekend, but Diandra knew her teacher would not accept their visit as a good excuse. "I know," thought Diandra, "I'll just say I was sick all weekend. Then she will give me one more day to do it."

What do you think might happen to Diandra if she lies to her teacher?

_____

_____

5 Read two of the following Bible verses from the book of Proverbs. Then write down what you learned.

Proverbs 12:13	**Proverbs 12:19**	**Proverbs 12:22**
Proverbs 19:5	**Proverbs 21:6**	**Proverbs 24:28**

_____

_____

39

Date Used: _____

Group: _____

WHAT, ME LIE?
Topic: Lying

Purpose of this Session:

Preschoolers and younger children love to make up stories—to pretend. They have difficulty telling the difference between reality and fantasy. Most people don't worry about their half-truths. But during the 4th–6th grades, lying can become a serious problem and, if left unchecked, a dangerous pattern can develop. Lies at this age are like those of adults, often told to deceive, conceal, or manipulate. And lying leads to more lying. Use this TalkSheet to discuss the consequences of lying and the advantages of honesty.

To Introduce the Topic:

Before the meeting begins, ask three volunteer young people to write down four statements about themselves, three that are true and one that is false. Make sure these statements are in good taste. They can be about anything from the color of their eyes to where they spent their last summer vacations.

Have each kid read his or her statements to the group. After each kid finishes, challenge the group to pick the statement that is a lie. Announce that you will be talking about lying.

The Discussion:

Item #1: This question establishes the fact that kids lie. You do not need to admonish the young people when they begin admitting to all the lies they tell and to whom they tell them. In fact, research indicates that punishment, especially harsh punishment, does not deter kids from lying. Rather, it increases the incidences of lying.

Item #2: Explore all the reasons why kids lie as well as why adults lie. Then talk about the consequences of lying related to each of the reasons. For example, if someone lies to protect a friend, is the friend really protected, or can this kind of lie actually hurt a friend in the long run?

Item #3: Contrast the difference between how kids feel when someone lies to them versus being told the truth. Discuss the difference between how kids feel when they lie to others versus telling them the truth.

Item #4: Use this situation to discuss again the consequences of lying versus the advantages of honesty.

Item #5: You can also talk about our God of truth and honesty (Deuteronomy 32:4; 2 Samuel 7:28; Psalm 146:6) and how we can depend upon him and trust him because of this. Also talk about God's forgiveness when we lie.

To Close the Session:

Point out that God wants us to be honest because honesty protects us in the long run. Remind the group of the story of the boy who cried wolf. His word could no longer be trusted. This hurt him in the long run because when he needed the townspeople, no one believed him. Create a list with the group of all of the benefits of telling the truth. Encourage them to consider these benefits the next time they are tempted to lie. Young people need to know that honesty really is the best policy.

sel·fə·stēm

1 Matt thinks that he is stupid, clumsy, bad in sports, and that nobody likes him. Elisha thinks she is good at music, smart, kind of pretty, and a good friend. Matt does not feel very good about himself, but Elisha has a lot of self-confidence. **If you were to think of four things about yourself, would you think of bad stuff like Matt or good stuff like Elisha?**

_____ **Good stuff**   _____ **Not so good stuff**   _____ **Bad stuff**

2 Self-esteem is something you will hear much about over the next few years as you grow up. Self-esteem is how people see themselves. Give a definition of what it means to you by completing the following sentence: **Self-esteem is . . .**

_____

_____

3 Read each of the following statements, then decide if each is something you do none of the time, some of the time, most of the time, or all of the time.

a. I appreciate and care about myself.

_____ **None of the time**   _____ **Most of the time**
_____ **Some of the time**   _____ **All of the time**

b. I believe others when they say good things about me.

_____ **None of the time**   _____ **Most of the time**
_____ **Some of the time**   _____ **All of the time**

c. I accept God's love for me.

_____ **None of the time**   _____ **Most of the time**
_____ **Some of the time**   _____ **All of the time**

d. I realize that God created me as a unique and special person.

_____ **None of the time**   _____ **Most of the time**
_____ **Some of the time**   _____ **All of the time**

e. I feel good about the things I accomplish at school.

_____ **None of the time**   _____ **Most of the time**
_____ **Some of the time**   _____ **All of the time**

f. I realize that I do not have to be good at everything.

_____ **None of the time**   _____ **Most of the time**
_____ **Some of the time**   _____ **All of the time**

4 Read the following verses and decide what message they have in common.

Genesis 1:27   **Psalm 24:1**   **Luke 12:7**   **John 1:12**

_____

_____

Date Used: _____

Group:_____

(sel–fə–stēm)
Topic: Self-esteem

Purpose of this Session:
Children derive their self-esteem largely from their parents and other caregivers when they are young. As they move into school, their peer groups increasingly play a significant role in providing them with a picture of themselves. Each of us receives feedback from those around us that helps shape how we perceive who we are. It is this perception that defines our self-esteem rather than actual reality. Young people may feel ugly, dumb, and weird, or good-looking, smart, and normal, depending upon the feedback they have received from their families, friends, important adults in their lives, and the media. Preadolescence marks a time that can be difficult on a young person's self-esteem. Use this opportunity to talk and listen to your kids concerning how they perceive their worth.

To Introduce the Topic:
Have the group complete the following sentence: "The one thing I would change about myself if I could is. . . ."

The Discussion:
Item #1: Most young people will say that they would think of good stuff. Affirm the young people in their constructive views of themselves. Then talk about what young people can positively do and where they can go when they don't feel so good about themselves. Explain that the church is the community of God where they can find God's grace.

Item #2: Arrive at a group definition. Talk with the group about why people talk so much about self-esteem.

Item #3: Each of these statements can be discussed individually as part of a healthy self-image. Make a list with the group of all the things that young people have control over that can help them raise their self-esteem. Examples are to talk about their feelings, to follow through on tasks they begin, to set goals and work toward them, to talk with a parent or a trustworthy adult about the things that are important to them, to ask for forgiveness when they are wrong, to list their strengths and weaknesses and accept them both, and so on.

Item #4: Discuss how a relationship with Christ affects one's self-esteem.

To Close the Session:
God created all of us in his image. This means that we are special and significant. Sin did not take this specialness away, although our sin did mar our being. The fall in the garden did not make us nonpeople. Sinful does not equal worthless. It did not take away from our worth and dignity in the eyes of God. He chose to redeem us through the death on the cross of his Son, Jesus Christ. Not only are we a special creation of God's, but he loves us deeply. We need to balance our sinfulness with our significance. We are worthwhile, but this does not make us good. We are still sinners in need of a savior. We tend to emphasize one without the other. Each of us is valued and esteemed in God's eyes. He is "not wanting anyone to perish, but everyone to come to repentance" (2 Peter 3:9).

HANDI-CAPABLE

1 Circle the problems in the following list that you feel are handicaps:

Mental retardation	**Allergies**	**A speech problem**
Deafness	**Wearing a leg brace**	**Cerebral palsy**
A missing toe	**A slight limp**	**Asthma**
Epilepsy	**Dyslexia**	**Paralysis**
Muscular dystrophy	**Diabetes**	**Wearing glasses**
Blindness	**A missing leg**	**Quadriplegia**
Obesity	**A birthmark on your arm**	**Wearing braces or a retainer**

2 Go back to Item #1 and look at the problems you circled. Put an **X** through those you believe would be really **difficult** to have.

3 I believe kids with disabilities are . . .

_____ **different than I am.**
_____ **similar to me.**

4 For each of the problems listed below, decide how likely it would be for you to start a friendship with a kid who had the problem. (Circle either **NO WAY, MAYBE,** or **FOR SURE.**)

Mental retardation	**NO WAY**	**MAYBE**	**FOR SURE**
Deafness	**NO WAY**	**MAYBE**	**FOR SURE**
A missing toe	**NO WAY**	**MAYBE**	**FOR SURE**
Blindness	**NO WAY**	**MAYBE**	**FOR SURE**
Obesity	**NO WAY**	**MAYBE**	**FOR SURE**
Allergies	**NO WAY**	**MAYBE**	**FOR SURE**
Wearing a leg brace	**NO WAY**	**MAYBE**	**FOR SURE**
A slight limp	**NO WAY**	**MAYBE**	**FOR SURE**
A birthmark on an arm	**NO WAY**	**MAYBE**	**FOR SURE**
Quadriplegia	**NO WAY**	**MAYBE**	**FOR SURE**
A speech problem	**NO WAY**	**MAYBE**	**FOR SURE**
Cerebral palsy	**NO WAY**	**MAYBE**	**FOR SURE**
Asthma	**NO WAY**	**MAYBE**	**FOR SURE**
A missing leg	**NO WAY**	**MAYBE**	**FOR SURE**
Wearing glasses	**NO WAY**	**MAYBE**	**FOR SURE**

5 Place an **X** through one of the following set of numbers. The set of numbers you pick represents a Bible verse you will study. Your leader will tell you how to find your verse in the Bible.

1 20 11 17	2 2 1 41	2 3 10 33	2 6 15 1

Date Used: _____

Group: _____

HANDI-CAPABLE
Topic: Disabilities

Purpose of this Session:

Unfortunately, many kids often reject their peers who are disabled. This lack of acceptance harms the self-image and social relationships of those with disabilities and robs kids who are not disabled of growth experiences and valuable friendships. This TalkSheet gives your group the opportunity to talk about a Christian's response to disabilities.

To Introduce the Topic:

Before your meeting begins, take three members of your group aside and tell them that for the first few minutes of the discussion time they will each be given a disability. As in life, they can't choose their disabilities. Give a pair of glasses with petroleum jelly smeared on the lenses to the first young person. Tie the feet and the legs of the second youth together. And place a large, irregularly shaped red mark on the face of the third group member. Be sure to use a washable marker or a stick of clown makeup for easy removal.

Have the three group members sit in their usual places. Assist them when necessary to avoid injury. Begin the meeting, allowing it to go on for several minutes. Ask your newly disabled members to participate in typical activities. Ask the blinded person to read Scripture. The person with the disfigured red face can stand and lead the group in singing.

Begin your discussion by asking the three young people how it felt to be disabled for the beginning minutes of your group time. Remove their disabilities before beginning the discussion.

The Discussion:

Item #1: See which problems are considered handicaps and which are not. Explain to the group that there are people with disabilities, but these disabilities may or may not handicap them. A problem may be an inconvenience but that does not necessarily handicap the person experiencing it. A handicap is all in the perception of the person with the problem. A problem can also be perceived as a handicap by those who have not experienced the problem.

Item #2: Ask the kids if they know anyone with these difficult handicaps. Ask what makes these so difficult. Explore with your group members how they can be more accepting of kids who are experiencing these disabilities.

Item #3: Make a list of the differences and similarities. Make the observation that many of the differences are created by people who don't have the disabilities.

Item #4: Discuss with the group why, for many kids, a disability might interfere with a friendship. Turn the tables on the students by asking them to pretend that tomorrow they wake up with a disability. How might their friends react, and why? How would their new disability interfere with their capacity to be a friend?

Item #5: Explain that the first number represents the Old or New Testament (1 = Old Testament; 2 = New Testament), the second number represents the book of the Old or New Testament, the third number locates the chapter, and the fourth number indicates the verse. The three verses in order are Proverbs 11:17; Mark 1:41; Luke 10:33; and Romans 15:1. Ask for volunteers to read each of these verses. Also examine 2 Samuel 9:1–13 for the story of Mephibosheth, a man with a disability for whom King David had compassion.

To Close the Session:

Challenge your group members to accept people with disabilities with the love of Christ. All of us are created in God's image, no matter what our disabilities. And all of us need to be included in life.

CHANGING CHANNELS

1 List three of your most favorite and three of your least favorite TV shows.

MOST FAVORITE	LEAST FAVORITE
a. _____	a. _____
b. _____	b. _____
c. _____	c. _____

2 How much TV do you watch? (Put an **X** before the statement that applies to you.)

DURING THE WEEK	ON WEEKENDS
__ Less than most kids my age.	__ Less than most kids my age.
__ About the same as most kids my age.	__ About the same as most kids my age.
__ More than most kids my age.	__ More than most kids my age.

3 Answer the following questions to find out what your life might be like if you could not watch any television.

a. What would you do after dinner once your homework was done? _____

_____

b. What would you do on Saturday mornings? _____

_____

c. What would you do when the weather was bad and you had to stay inside? _____

_____

d. What would you do when your friends talked about TV shows? _____

_____

4 What rules do you have in your family regarding TV viewing?
(Circle all that apply.)

a. No TV is allowed.
b. I must ask a parent or guardian before watching.
c. No TV is allowed until homework is done.

d. Only a certain number of shows can be watched each day.
e. Other rules: _____
_____

5 Fill in the blank in the sentence below with the word *always, sometimes,* or *never.*
I _____ **watch television shows that I know are not good for me.**

6 Read **Ephesians 2:10** and answer the following question: **How can TV interfere with God's plan for you?** _____

_____

45

Date Used: _____

Group: _____

CHANGING CHANNELS
Topic: Television Viewing

Purpose of this Session:
Young people watch hours and hours of television every week. This generation of kids has been raised primarily on visual media. Since television has such a powerful influence on our children, use this TalkSheet to discuss with your kids how it is shaping their lives.

To Introduce the Topic:
Ask the group members to name all of the channels or stations they watch on television. Write each of these down on a chalkboard or on newsprint for everyone to see. This will give you the big picture concerning the general content of your group's television diet. See which stations are watched the most—public television, movie channels, sports, news, MTV, and so on. Take a poll to see how many kids live in homes with cable or satellite television. Also ask how many use VCRs to tape and view programs.

The Discussion:
Item #1: Young people will swap stories about their most and least favorite TV shows. Generally kids have an easier time thinking of their most favorite. Some kids may have only one or two favorites, which is okay. In fact, you want to affirm those kids who do not watch much television, but do so without making them look like nerds in front of their peers. Some young people will mention shows that others in the group are not allowed to watch. If this occurs you may hear "Your mom lets you watch that?" or "My dad won't let me watch that!" You do not want kids to put each other down for what can or can't be watched. If this happens use it as an opportunity to talk about appropriate content. You could ask questions like, "Why might parents not want their children to watch _____?" or "Why do parents want their kids protected from certain TV shows?" When the kids have had a chance to share their choices, ask them what makes a program a most or least favorite.

Item #2: Explore why kids watch so much television. You may have a wide variety of responses, from the kid who says, "Our family doesn't own a TV" to the child who states, "Our TV is on all day."

Item #3: Take each question one at a time. You will have many kids say that they would go to their friends' homes to watch TV or that they would substitute other media, such as video games or radios. Explore alternatives other than the media, like playing, reading, church involvement, sports, family activities, and so on. Ask the kids what they would miss the most and why. You can tell the kids they sound like people who are trying to get off drugs in their "withdrawal" comments. Ask how healthy this really is.

Item #4: Talk about the fairness and unfairness of each of the rules. Use this opportunity to support parents in their quest to monitor and sensibly use the television. Ask the kids to create their own list of rules they think would be pleasing to God.

Item #5: Most kids will declare they always or sometimes watch television shows that they know are not good for them. Explore what they mean by a TV show not being good for them. The kids will say things like, "I learn bad words" or "There is too much violence." Ask how negatively influenced we are by what we watch on television. Young people do not believe these shows will adversely affect them. Create a list of negative consequences from viewing these programs (more comfortable with violence, don't get exercise, don't learn to study).

Item #6: Many kids have never considered God in their TV viewing. Explore with the students the plans God has for them, for the present as well as the future. Then discuss how TV can hurt what God wants them to do. Some responses are that TV encourages them to put off doing their homework, it teaches them things that are wrong, commercials teach them to be materialistic, TV takes them away from their families, and so on.

To Close the Session:
Summarize what has been covered during the discussion. Then ask the group to plan a week of TV viewing for a pretend average fourth, fifth, or sixth grader. Use a TV listings booklet from your local newspaper or a TV Guide to help. Take into account all the other activities your pretend kid is involved in. You can then create a large Monday through Sunday schedule on the chalkboard or on newsprint. This gives you the chance to guide the students to think about their TV choices.

"!#*X/#" AND OTHER WORDS

1 How many kids use swear words at your school? (Circle only one answer.)

Very few kids
Some kids
About half of the kids
Most of the kids
All of the kids

Now go back and put a box around the number of kids at your school who take God's name in vain.

2 Place an **X** in front of the statements below that you believe explain why kids at your school use swear words.

_____ Kids use swear words because it gets them attention.

_____ Kids use swear words to make adults mad.

_____ Kids use swear words because adults like kids to use them.

_____ Kids use swear words so other kids will think they are cool.

_____ Kids use swear words to show how grown-up they think they are.

_____ Kids use swear words because it is fun.

_____ Kids use swear words _____.
(give another reason here)

3 In the following sentences, fill in the blanks with the words *should* or *should not*.

a. A kid _____ be allowed to watch movies that contain swear words.

b. A kid _____ be allowed to use swear words around other kids.

c. A kid _____ be allowed to listen to music with swear words.

d. A kid _____ be allowed to have friends who use swear words.

4 What would you do if someone you were with used swear words?

_____

_____

5 Place an **X** through one of the following set of numbers. The set of numbers you pick represents a Bible verse you will study. Your leader will tell you how to find your verse in the Bible.

1 20 15 28　　　　**2 10 5 4**　　　　**2 11 4 8**

Date Used: _____

Group: _____

"!#*X/#" AND OTHER WORDS
Topic: Profanity

Purpose of this Session:

Profanity and taking the Lord's name in vain have become common on the elementary school playground. Children have had good teachers—today's adults. In past generations, adults used bad language, but they protected kids from it. Today this is no longer true. Kids need an opportunity to talk with adults about the use of profanity and how it can adversely affect them.

To Introduce the Topic:

Ask the group members to list a number of movies (either presently showing in theaters or available for home rental) popular with their age group. Write these down on newsprint or on a chalkboard for everyone to see. Then ask the group to identify those movies that contain swear words. Circle these as group members identify them. Point out how many of today's popular movies contain swear words. Affirm and support those group members who have not seen many of the movies that contain profanity. You do not want to support these movies; rather, you want to point out that these movies are adversely affecting your group members. Do not talk about these negative effects at this time. Use the session closure time to call attention to the detrimental effects of today's popular movies. Tell the group you will be talking about profanity. Pass out the TalkSheets and ask the kids to fill them out as honestly as they can.

SPECIAL NOTE: Be careful if you choose to use profanity during the discussion. It can be appropriate to use examples of profanity but not to shock kids. When profanity is used as an example, it can demonstrate that you know the words. This takes the fun and mystery out of the words. You do not have to use the words as examples, but avoid the mistake of elevating the words to the totally forbidden. When talking about the profane, we can avoid the words to such a degree that it becomes enticing and exciting to use profanity.

SPECIAL, SPECIAL NOTE: Many kids have parents who curse and misuse God's name on a regular basis. This can be confusing to children when you talk about the negative effects of profanity. Mention to the group that some parents do curse, but this does not make it appropriate for kids to curse. Some parents smoke, but this does not make it right or healthy for kids to do so.

The Discussion:

Item #1: Poll the group to see the extent that profanity is used by kids. Ask the kids, "When you hear profanity, what do you usually think?" Ask kids if they would misuse God's name or use profanity if God were around. Point out that God is with us. We tend to forget where God is.

Item #2: Have the group decide the three most popular reasons kids use bad words. Some additional reasons might be to get more friends, to be a part of the group, to show off, to be like their parents, or because they are mad.

Item #3: If most of the group members feel that kids should be allowed to watch movies that contain profanity (and many will), you will need to support those kids who feel that they should not be allowed. Take time to discuss the swearing in movies. Pay special attention to the statement, "A kid ___ be allowed to use swear words around other kids." Often young people believe bad language is appropriate as long as it is not used around adults.

Item #4: Brainstorm with the group all of the possible responses, from ignoring the profanity to asking that person not to use bad language. You may want to role-play responses with the kids.

Item #5: Explain that the first number represents the Old or New Testament (1 = Old Testament; 2 = New Testament), the second number represents the book of the Old or New Testament, the third number locates the chapter, and the fourth number indicates the verse. The three verses in order are Proverbs 15:28; Ephesians 5:4; and Philippians 4:8. Ask for volunteers to read each of these verses. Discuss how each relates to the use of bad language. Also look at the third commandment (Exodus 20:7) to discuss misusing God's name.

To Close the Session:

Make a list with the kids of the adverse effects of profanity. The following is a sample of some negative effects:

1. We become so comfortable with profanity that it becomes a part of us.
2. Profanity puts others down.
3. Using profanity is an inappropriate way to deal with anger. We need to learn more constructive ways to deal with anger.
4. Profanity hurts people.
5. The misuse of God's name hurts our relationship with God.
6. Cursing demonstrates how immature we are.

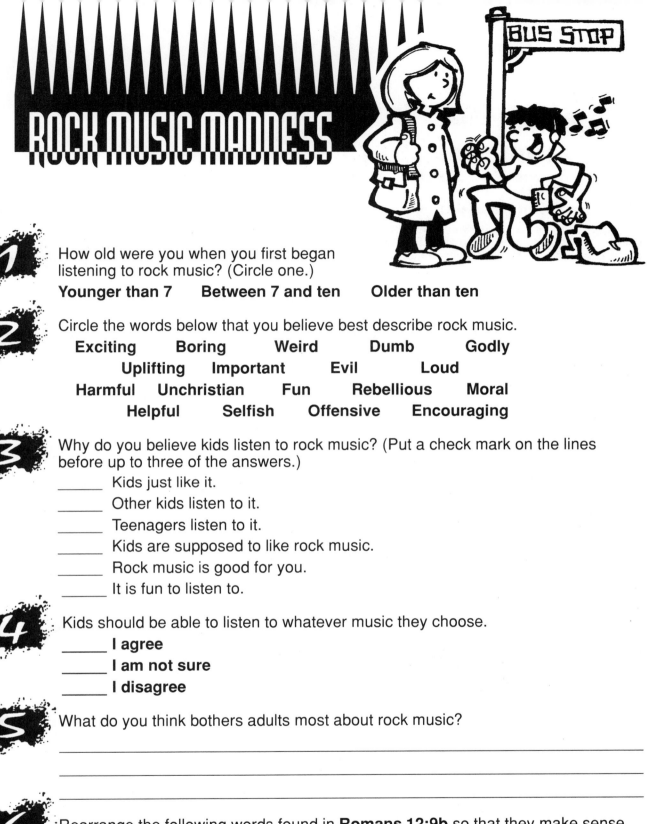

ROCK MUSIC MADNESS

1 How old were you when you first began listening to rock music? (Circle one.)

Younger than 7   Between 7 and ten   Older than ten

2 Circle the words below that you believe best describe rock music.

Exciting   Boring   Weird   Dumb   Godly

Uplifting   Important   Evil   Loud

Harmful   Unchristian   Fun   Rebellious   Moral

Helpful   Selfish   Offensive   Encouraging

3 Why do you believe kids listen to rock music? (Put a check mark on the lines before up to three of the answers.)

_____ Kids just like it.

_____ Other kids listen to it.

_____ Teenagers listen to it.

_____ Kids are supposed to like rock music.

_____ Rock music is good for you.

_____ It is fun to listen to.

4 Kids should be able to listen to whatever music they choose.

_____ **I agree**

_____ **I am not sure**

_____ **I disagree**

5 What do you think bothers adults most about rock music?

_____

_____

_____

6 Rearrange the following words found in **Romans 12:9b** so that they make sense.

evil; what is to what good. cling Hate is

_____

Date Used: _____

Group: _____

ROCK MUSIC MADNESS
Topic: Rock-and-Roll Music

Purpose of this Session:

One normally thinks of teenagers when the phrase rock and roll is used. But the music listening habits of young people are no longer formed during adolescence. It is now during the preadolescent years that young people begin to develop their rock music listening patterns. Young people at this age are aware of the radio stations that play Top 40, rap, hard rock, and, of course, the oldie rock music that many of their parents still listen to.

Instead of waiting until the teen years to talk about the good, the bad, and the ugly in rock music, use this TalkSheet to lead a balanced rock music discussion.

To Introduce the Topic:

You will need to first define rock music with your group. Fans of heavy metal don't consider rap to be rock music, pop rock (Top 40 stuff) is not seen as real rock by hard rockers, and so on. For the purposes of this discussion, rock music is the music normally listened to by teenagers. This definition includes pop, heavy metal, punk, rap, and all other types of popular teenage/young adult music.

Take the rock music pulse of your group members by asking them to brainstorm a list of the rock music radio stations in your area, the popular rock bands of the day, a line of lyrics from a number of popular songs, the names of popular Christian rock artists, scenes from popular rock music videos, and the like. This can be an indicator of how involved your group is in the world of rock music.

The Discussion:

Item #1: You do not need to spend much time on this item. Its intent is to listen to the kids' perceptions of when they began to listen to rock. You can ask them how they feel this has affected them.

Item #2: In using this TalkSheet, it has been our unscientific observation that kids who circled "younger than 7" in Item #1 tend to circle words like exciting, fun, helpful, and uplifting. Those who circled "older than ten" are more likely to circle boring, weird, evil, dumb, and harmful. It seems that kids who begin listening when they are older are able to use more discernment skills in choosing what they listen to. We have also noticed that kids who are not as into the rock scene feel pressured to agree with their peers, and they may erase or not list responses like evil. Use your discussion time to talk about how all of these words describe rock music. You can introduce the concept of discernment here.

Item #3: Explore with the students the different reasons they believe kids listen to rock music. Ask the group to pick the top three reasons. This TalkSheet is titled "Rock Music Madness" because kids and teenagers too often listen to music with little thought to discernment. Use the title to explore this observation.

Item #4: Many, if not most, young people will agree with this statement. Talk with them about how they choose what they listen to and why making wise rock music listening choices is important.

Item #5: Answers to this question will include the beat, the bad words, or the volume. Again, reiterate the importance of discernment skills.

Item #6: This passage is not anti-rock; rather, it is pro making wise decisions. Ask the kids how this applies to their music choices. Ask the following question: "If Jesus were to listen with you to your music, what comments might he make?"

To Close the Session:

Lecturing kids about the evils of rock music or throwing out Bible verses that condemn their music is counterproductive and leads to many unintended negative consequences. Adults will make more headway influencing young people for Christ by challenging kids to carefully choose what they listen to. Take a few minutes to analyze some of the popular songs. You will find that some are very uplifting and positive, some are harmless, and some are downright evil.

Affirm those kids who have taken a stand during the discussion and talked about making wise choices. You do not want your young people to get the impression that they should listen to any and all rock music, just because many kids do.

If you wish to lead additional discussions on rock music, a good resource is *Rock Talk: The Active Rock Music Discussion Game* by David Lynn (published by Zondervan Publishing House/Youth Specialties).

RATED K FOR KIDS

1 List the titles of the last three movies you watched, either at the theater or on video.

a. _____

b. _____

c. _____

2 Circle each of the types of rated movies that you have personally watched.

G-rated movies   **R-rated movies**

PG-rated movies   **NC-17-rated movies**

PG 13-rated movies   **X-rated movies**

3 Cross out with an **X** the kinds of movies listed below that kids should not watch.

Movies parent disapproves of	PG 13-rated movies	Cartoons
Movies focused on violence	Movies with nudity	Science fiction movies
Movies with drugs involved	Horror movies	Westerns
Blood and gore movies	Family movies	R-rated movies
Movies with bad language	Adventure movies	Murder movies

4 How do you choose the kinds of movies you watch? _____

_____

_____

5 Put a check mark in front of the statement that you feel is right.

____ A kid should never have to talk with a parent about the movies she or he watches.

____ A kid should only talk about a movie when a parent asks.

____ A kid should talk with a parent about some movies she or he watches.

____ A kid should talk with a parent about every movie she or he watches.

6 Read the following scrambled verse found in **Colossians 2:8** by using the numbers, beginning with #1. Then write out what you believe the passage says about watching movies.

   4. **the basic principles of this world**
   2. **through hollow and deceptive philosophy,**
   5. **rather than on Christ.**
   1. **See to it that no one takes you captive**
   3. **which depends on human tradition and**

_____

RATED K FOR KIDS
Topic: Movies

Purpose of this Session:

Home video rental and cable TV have opened a new world to children. At a young age, kids are watching everything from family entertainment to blood and gore, often without much guidance. When asked, today's 4th–6th graders will tell you that kids younger than they are watching even worse. This TalkSheet can help your kids take a good, hard look at the movies they are watching. The purpose here is not to condemn movie watching but to encourage better discernment of what is watched.

To Introduce the Topic:

Bring the movie section of your local paper with you to the group. Tell the kids you want to read some of the movie ads to them and get their responses. Read the ads including the names of the actors and actresses, the ratings, the music groups, and so on. Pause for a second or two to hear the responses, then move on to another ad. Tell the group you will be discussing movies.

The Discussion:

Item #1: Make a group list of all the films that your kids report that they have seen. Place this list on a chalkboard for everyone to see.

Item #2: Most of the kids will have watched four of the six rating types. Explore with the group members why they believe a rating system exists. Explain that ratings are given to provide information to parents about the content of movies. A group of adults rates movies to protect kids from things grown-ups believe kids should not see without some parental guidance. Ask the students if they believe the rating system rates movies correctly. Have the kids go through the movie list created in Item #1 and rate the movies the way they believe they should be rated. They can use an NC-17 or even an X if they so desire.

Item #3: Ask kids how they arrived at their decisions. Do they apply this reasoning to their own movie and television viewing?

Item #4: Kids will say things like, "If my parents let me go see it or rent it," "If it is funny," or "If the previews looked good." Here is an opportunity to talk about discernment. Ask the group members what criteria God would want them to use in selecting the movies they watch. Create a list of all the ways they can decide which movies are helpful and which are harmful. This is best done in the form of questions: How will the movie affect my attitude toward God? What would my parents think of me watching this film?

Item #5: Kids often resist talking with their parents about the content of movies. Explore with the young people the benefits and disadvantages of talking with parents about the movies they see. There will be a variety of parental standards represented by your group. Some kids get to watch almost anything they want with little or no processing and guidance by the parents. Others are restricted from watching almost any movie. Talk about and encourage discussion with adults about movie content.

Item #6: Create a list of all the ways harmful movies take kids captive through their hollow and deceptive philosophy. Another passage your group will find useful to discuss is 1 John 4:1.

To Close the Session:

Ask the kids how they feel about adults protecting them with ratings. Are the ratings working to protect them? Why do adults feel kids need to be protected? How does God want kids protected? How can kids protect themselves?

UP IN SMOKE

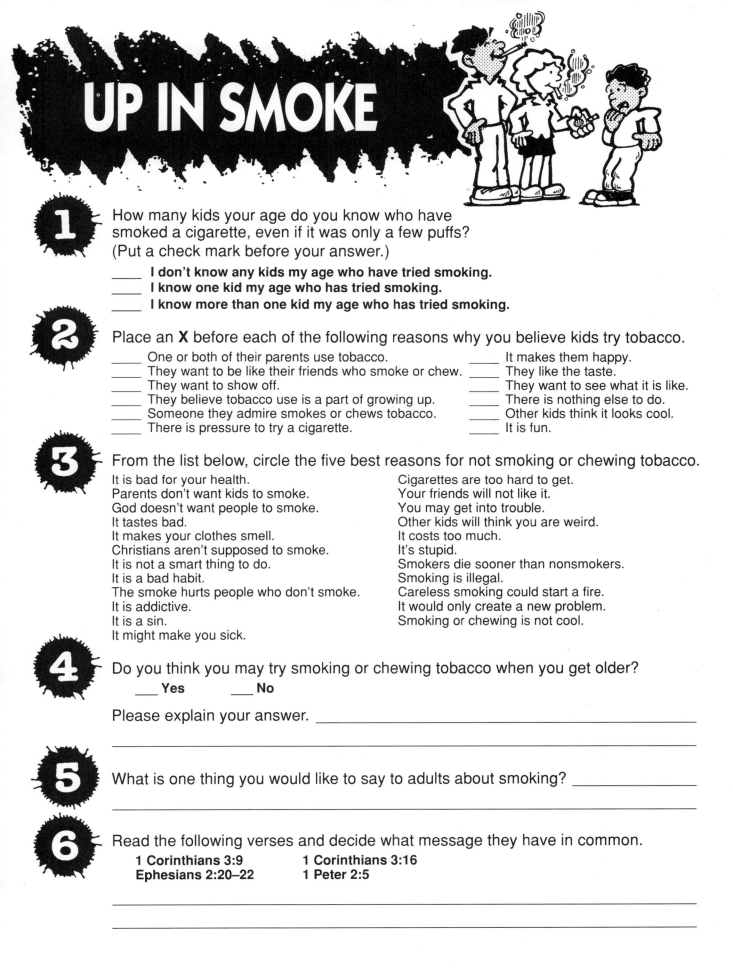

1 How many kids your age do you know who have
smoked a cigarette, even if it was only a few puffs?
(Put a check mark before your answer.)

_____ **I don't know any kids my age who have tried smoking.**
_____ **I know one kid my age who has tried smoking.**
_____ **I know more than one kid my age who has tried smoking.**

2 Place an **X** before each of the following reasons why you believe kids try tobacco.

_____ One or both of their parents use tobacco.   _____ It makes them happy.
_____ They want to be like their friends who smoke or chew. _____ They like the taste.
_____ They want to show off.   _____ They want to see what it is like.
_____ They believe tobacco use is a part of growing up.   _____ There is nothing else to do.
_____ Someone they admire smokes or chews tobacco.   _____ Other kids think it looks cool.
_____ There is pressure to try a cigarette.   _____ It is fun.

3 From the list below, circle the five best reasons for not smoking or chewing tobacco.

It is bad for your health.   Cigarettes are too hard to get.
Parents don't want kids to smoke.   Your friends will not like it.
God doesn't want people to smoke.   You may get into trouble.
It tastes bad.   Other kids will think you are weird.
It makes your clothes smell.   It costs too much.
Christians aren't supposed to smoke.   It's stupid.
It is not a smart thing to do.   Smokers die sooner than nonsmokers.
It is a bad habit.   Smoking is illegal.
The smoke hurts people who don't smoke. Careless smoking could start a fire.
It is addictive.   It would only create a new problem.
It is a sin.   Smoking or chewing is not cool.
It might make you sick.

4 Do you think you may try smoking or chewing tobacco when you get older?
_____ **Yes**   _____ **No**

Please explain your answer. _____

_____

5 What is one thing you would like to say to adults about smoking? _____

_____

6 Read the following verses and decide what message they have in common.
1 Corinthians 3:9   **1 Corinthians 3:16**
Ephesians 2:20–22   **1 Peter 2:5**

_____

_____

Date Used: _____

Group: _____

UP IN SMOKE
Topic: Nicotine Use

Purpose of this Session:

It is not the purpose of this discussion to condemn those who smoke, be they parents, relatives, schoolteachers, or church children's workers. Condemning smokers rather than voicing opposition to smoking can be confusing to young people, especially those whose parents and other adults close to them smoke. Use this discussion time to focus on what is in the best interests of your kids. You will need to take time to discuss the addictive nature of tobacco as the reason adults who smoke have such a difficult time quitting. Point out that most adults who do smoke would like to quit but can't. An addiction to tobacco is one of the most powerful addictions known.

To Introduce the Topic:

Collect several magazine cigarette ads that you can show the kids. Ask the group what messages these ads communicate to young people, then read the warning labels contained in the ads. Ask the group how these warning labels contradict the message being put forth by the cigarette companies. Ask which message is closer to the truth.

The Discussion:

Item #1: You will have a variety of responses depending upon the makeup of your group. This item indicates the potential peer influence for or against smoking in your community. As you begin your discussion, you will find it helpful to know that there is a significant correlation between parental smoking and a child's experimentation with smoking. Also, the children of smokers are more inclined to hold more positive attitudes toward smoking than the kids of nonsmokers.

Item #2: Ask the young people to look through the reasons and decide if any of them are good reasons to smoke. A great many young people try cigarettes or chew because they want to feel grown-up. Many of these reasons are legitimate needs kids have, but smoking won't meet those needs. Check the list again and determine how those that are needs can be met in more constructive ways.

Item #3: Let kids add any reasons not found on the list. Point out that there are many good reasons not to smoke and really no good reasons to smoke, yet young people every day try smoking. Explore with the group why this is so.

Item #4: Most kids will answer no to this question. Some may already have tried it, and some may say yes. Do not use this item to morally beat kids over the head. Rather, take this opportunity to reinforce saying no to smoking. Research indicates that young people who have puffed on cigarettes as children are more likely to further experiment as they grow up. Take this opportunity to help shape a more positive attitude toward saying no.

Item #5: This item helps young people affirm a negative stand toward the use of tobacco.

Item #6: Ask the group to write a statement that summarizes the passages of Scripture.

To Close the Session:

Summarize what has been said during your discussion. You will not want to preach against smoking as much as you want to emphasize what is in the best interests of your kids. Lecturing against the evils of smoking only serves to push kids toward the thing you want them to avoid.

BOTHERED CONCERNED AGITATED
WORRIED TROUBLED
FRAZZLED TORMENTED

1 Fill in the blank in the sentence below with the phrase *a lot* or the phrase *very little*.

Kids have _____ to worry about in today's world.

2 Mark an **X** next to all the things on the following list that you worry about from time to time.

___ Failing	___ Being pressured by parents or guardians
___ Being teased	___ Disagreeing with parents or guardians
___ Becoming a teenager	___ How violent the world is
___ How I look	___ What friends think of me
___ Being criticized	___ Having parents divorce
___ Having a parent dying	___ Having something bad happen to me
___ Getting into trouble	___ World problems, like hunger or war
___ Losing a friend	___ What God thinks of me
___ Living in a polluted world	___ Having problems with a brother or a sister
___ Making mistakes	___ Being picked on by a bully
___ Having school problems	___ Dealing with alcohol and drugs
___ What the future holds	___ Not having enough money

3 Why do you think kids your age worry so much about school? (Circle your top three choices.)

Lots of homework	Tough teachers
Need to get good grades	Want to please parents
Sports are too hard	No one cares
Problems with school friends	Hard homework
Hard tests	Pressure from other students
Too much to learn	Gangs
Fights	Something else:_____

4 Have you ever worried so much you could not get to sleep right away when you went to bed?

___ **Yes**   ___ **No**

5 Rearrange the following words found in **1 Peter 5:7** so that they make sense.

Cast cares anxiety on all him your he for because you.

_____

BOTHERED CONCERNED AGITATED WORRIED TROUBLED
FRAZZLED TORMENTED
Topic: Worrying

Purpose of this Session:

Today's kids contradict conventional wisdom. Conventional wisdom has taught that kids don't worry like adults. After all, they are only kids. But today's kids are very much aware of adult problems and even global concerns. Kids face adult-sized problems before they are capable of handling them. Unfortunately, many young people have not yet realized that God can see them through their worries. They need not worry alone. Use this TalkSheet to examine the worries of kids in your group, and explore with them the reality of God's availability to them as a source of help and comfort.

To Introduce the Topic:

Ask the young people to make a list of all the things that they worried about or feared when they were much younger. This list can be created on the chalkboard or on newsprint. You will be recording fears like being afraid of the dark, crossing the street, monsters, strangers, bad people, thunder, and so on. Then tell the students you will be discussing the worries they now have as kids. Pass out the TalkSheets and ask the group to fill them out.

The Discussion:

Item #1: Adults tend to underestimate how much kids worry as well as the amount of issues that cause kids to worry. Kids worry a lot! Explore with the group members why they believe they have more to worry about. They will talk about how their parents did not have to lock the doors, things were cheaper, the world was not as polluted, and so on. Validate the fact that your kids do have a lot of worries. Do not discount their worries or put them down in any way. You can say something like, "Young people really do have too much to worry about today!" Technically, you were never their age in the sense that you are not 10, 11, or 12 today. What kids need are understanding and sympathetic, rather than critical, adults.

Item #2: Ask the young people to go back over the list and circle all the issues they have worried about in the past week. Probe with the group why these are things that many kids worry about.

Item #3: School and school-related activities and issues are near the top of the worry list with kids (family is often at the top). Take this opportunity to let kids talk about their many concerns related to school. Kids feel pressured by homework, tests, conflict with teachers—the list goes on and on. Let this activity provide a time of catharsis where your group members feel safe in "dumping" their school worries on the group.

Item #4: Most kids will answer yes to this question. Talk about how we can worry ourselves sick. Use this as an opportunity to brainstorm strategies to positively cope with worries. Ask kids to decide which of the following are good ways to handle situations they worry about:

Blame others	Do nothing since nothing can be done
Talk with a parent	Figure out a way to solve the problem
Put yourself down	See the positive side of things
Get really mad	Talk with a trustworthy adult
Fight back	Figure out a way to make the best of the situation
Talk with God	Do something to take your mind off your worries, such as watch TV
Scream and yell	Try to forget about the situation
Get really depressed	Say nothing about the problem
Talk with a friend	Wish that the worry would go away

Obviously, the more control kids have over situations, the more active they can be at coping with them. Many times the things kids worry about are beyond their control, like a parental divorce. In these cases, kids must figure out ways to make the best of their situations.

Item #5: The passage in the NIV reads "Cast all your anxiety on him because he cares for you." Explain to the group that we cannot easily throw away our problems, but we can throw away the anxiety those problems create in us. God tells us to throw our anxiety that results from our worries on him. He wants it because he loves us and cares about us. We can have confidence that God does care because he sent Christ to die for us. Act now and throw your anxiety on God's back!

To Close the Session:

Close by putting 1 Peter 5:7 into practice. Have the kids throw their anxieties onto God through a group prayer.

THE I CARE PROJECT

1 Circle the following examples of caring projects that you know exist in your community or church.

Animal shelter
Nursing home volunteer program
Shelter for the homeless
Clothing collection
Mentally retarded ministry
Christmas gifts for the needy

Food collection
Recycling aluminum cans
Tutoring for kids
Hospital visitation
Sponsoring a needy child
Prison ministry

2 Kids are too young to do anything important for Jesus Christ in making the world a better place to live.

_____ I agree   _____ I am not sure   _____ I disagree

3 Write down in the box below the name of a caring project that interests you.

Now answer the following questions about your chosen project:

a. **Are there any good reasons you should say no to helping with this project?** _____
_____

b. **How would your involvement in this project help you grow as a Christian?** _____
_____

c. **How would this project make a difference for Jesus Christ?**_____
_____

d. **What would your parents think of your helping with this project?** _____
_____

e. **How could you get involved in this project?** _____
_____

4 Why do more kids not get involved in caring projects?
_____

5 Read the following verses and decide what message they have in common.
Isaiah 1:17   Titus 3:8   Job 29:15, 16   Zechariah 7:9, 10
_____
_____

Date Used: _____

Group: _____

THE I CARE PROJECT
Topic: Christian Social Action

Purpose of this Session:
Christ has called Christians to the task of transforming the world. We make a grave error in focusing only on personal salvation (Romans 3:23, 24) and transformation (Romans 12:2). The kingdom of God (Matthew 4:17), or a transformed world that takes seriously the love, forgiveness, justice, and mercy spoken of by Christ, is the will of God for our society now, not just in the hereafter. Use this TalkSheet to examine the role kids can play as God's servants in transforming society.

To Introduce the Topic:
Bring with you to the group meeting a number of recent newspapers. Pass these out to small groups of kids. Tell the kids they have three minutes to look through the papers and identify as many societal problems as they can within the time limit. Give each group a piece of paper and a pencil to write down the identified problems. List these problems on a chalkboard or on newsprint as kids read them aloud, one group at a time.

The Discussion:
Item #1: Have the group members list additional caring projects that exist in their community and church. Explore with the group what your community would be like if none of these caring projects existed.

Item #2: Young people believe they can sometimes make a difference, but they are skeptical about the state of the world. They have been exposed at school and through the media to a world filled with crime, pollution, and problems. Ask for examples of how kids can make a difference. Refer back to the problems identified in the introductory activity, and ask which ones young people could help solve.

Item #3: After discussing each of the questions, take one or two projects the kids might want to do together and plan out, step by step, what they'll need to do for the caring projects to be successful.

Item #4: You will also want to discuss why more adults don't get involved in caring projects.

Item #5: Justice, mercy, and compassion to the oppressed are not common sermon themes, but they are the will of God. Examine these concepts with the kids, and ask why these are important to God.

To Close the Session:
Return to your newspaper problems and explore further how Christians can have a major impact on these societal problems. End with a reading and short discussion of the parable of the good Samaritan found in Luke 10:29–37.

Challenge the young people to get involved. Tell the kids that in the past there was a motto that said kids should be seen and not heard, but today young people are needed to help change the world for Jesus Christ.

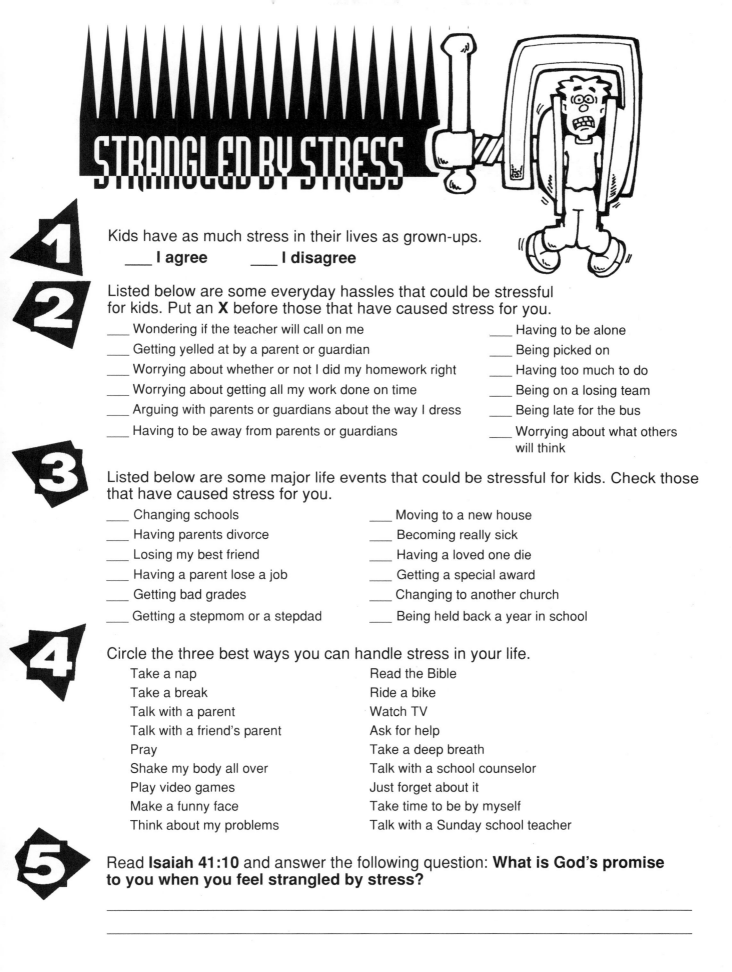

STRANGLED BY STRESS

1 Kids have as much stress in their lives as grown-ups.

___ **I agree**   ___ **I disagree**

2 Listed below are some everyday hassles that could be stressful for kids. Put an **X** before those that have caused stress for you.

___ Wondering if the teacher will call on me

___ Getting yelled at by a parent or guardian

___ Worrying about whether or not I did my homework right

___ Worrying about getting all my work done on time

___ Arguing with parents or guardians about the way I dress

___ Having to be away from parents or guardians

___ Having to be alone

___ Being picked on

___ Having too much to do

___ Being on a losing team

___ Being late for the bus

___ Worrying about what others will think

3 Listed below are some major life events that could be stressful for kids. Check those that have caused stress for you.

___ Changing schools

___ Having parents divorce

___ Losing my best friend

___ Having a parent lose a job

___ Getting bad grades

___ Getting a stepmom or a stepdad

___ Moving to a new house

___ Becoming really sick

___ Having a loved one die

___ Getting a special award

___ Changing to another church

___ Being held back a year in school

4 Circle the three best ways you can handle stress in your life.

Take a nap

Take a break

Talk with a parent

Talk with a friend's parent

Pray

Shake my body all over

Play video games

Make a funny face

Think about my problems

Read the Bible

Ride a bike

Watch TV

Ask for help

Take a deep breath

Talk with a school counselor

Just forget about it

Take time to be by myself

Talk with a Sunday school teacher

5 Read **Isaiah 41:10** and answer the following question: **What is God's promise to you when you feel strangled by stress?**

_____

_____

STRANGLED BY STRESS
Topic: Childhood Stress

Purpose of this Session:

A hot topic in teaching circles is childhood stress. Teachers see the symptoms of stress in their students—sleeping problems, nervous behavior, teeth grinding, upset stomachs, restlessness, uncontrollable crying, and more. Kids are now faced with adult-strength stress in large doses. This TalkSheet provides you with a forum for listening to your kids in a Christian context and brainstorming with them strategies for handling the stress they face.

To Introduce the Topic:

Play a quick, stress-object-lesson game with your group. You can use tennis balls or wads of newspaper to play this. Ask your group to sit in circles of five to seven people each (adults and young people mixed together). Each group member is given a wad of paper or a tennis ball. At the signal, the members of each small circled group are to roll their tennis balls or toss their wads of paper to other members of their group.

The object of the game is to keep the tennis balls or wads of paper moving. After a short and crazy period of time, stop the action. Then introduce an additional tennis ball or wad of newspaper so that everyone now has two. Begin the game again. Then add a third and fourth tennis ball or wad of paper.

End this stress-filled game, and tell the group you will be discussing the topic of stress.

The Discussion:

Item #1: This item validates the fact that kids face adult-strength stress. Listen to the kids as they tell their stress stories. You can also examine how adults make the lives of kids more or less stressful.

Item #2: Poll your group and rank everyday hassles from most to least stressful. The group can add hassles not found on this list.

Item #3: The young people may want to list additional major life events they find stressful.

Kids today experience stressful events at different levels. You will find that some kids check only a minority of these major life events while other kids check a majority. Set an accepting climate by listening to each of the kids. Stop the group if others are not listening and go over the discussion ground rules. Group members need to know they can dump their stress stories at the feet of your group and find acceptance.

Item #4: Discuss the benefits of talking with others to cope with stress, especially for handling stress related to major life events. Point out the people at your church or club organization that the young people can approach to talk with. Also encourage the young people to dialogue with their parents.

Item #5: This encouraging passage points to God as a source of comfort and love. Describe how your own relationship with Jesus Christ has helped you cope with stress. Point out that God doesn't promise to take away the stress-producing events. Rather, God helps us change our perceptions so that what is stressful to others does not have to be so stressful to those who rest in the Lord.

To Close the Session:

You can end by relating to the group some strategies Christ used to deal with stress. Jesus referred to God's Word (Matthew 4:1–11); he took time to be alone (Luke 4:42); he spent time in prayer (Matthew 14:22, 23); and he talked with his friends about what troubled him (Mark 14:33, 34).

UPGRADED

1 Complete the following sentence: **I am looking forward to being in middle/junior high school because . . .**

_____

_____

2 Place an **X** on the lines before the following questions about entering middle/junior high school that are a concern to you.

____ Will homework be more difficult?
____ How will I get along with the older kids?
____ Will I be tempted to smoke?
____ How much privacy will I have in the shower?
____ Will I be bothered by gang members?
____ How tough will the classes be?
____ Will I have time to get to my classes?
____ Will I be pressured to do things that are wrong?

____ Will I get picked on?
____ Will I have problems with my locker?
____ How will I do at sports?
____ Will I dress the right way?
____ Will I be offered alcohol or drugs?
____ How difficult will it be to make friends?
____ Will I get into trouble?
____ Will it be hard to be a Christian?

_____

_____

_____

3 When you get into middle/junior high school, how involved will you be in your church?

_____ **I will be more involved than I am now.**

_____ **I will stay involved about the same as I am now.**

_____ **I will be less involved than I am now.**

4 What is one question you have about attending middle/junior high school that you would like answered? (Write out your question below.)

_____

_____

5 Read the following verses and decide what message they have in common.

1 Corinthians 3:1, 2 **Ephesians 4:14**
1 Peter 2:2 **2 Peter 3:18**

_____

_____

_____

Date Used: _____

Group: _____

UPGRADED
Topic: Transition to Middle/Junior High School

Purpose of this Session:

Excitement! Panic! Curiosity! Anxiety! All these words are descriptive of the transition to the next level of schooling kids face. No matter how the transition is managed in your community (fifth or sixth graders moving to middle school; sixth graders moving to junior high), the move to the next level worries and frightens kids. Kids fear everything from trouble with their lockers to their Christian faith being ridiculed. You can create a climate of acceptance and help kids cope with their transition fears by talking through this TalkSheet with them.

To Introduce the Topic:

Begin by revealing some of your own growing-up fears. This sets the tone for young people to also share their fears. Allow the group to swap concerns for a few minutes. Then announce that you want the young people to write letters to an eighth grader describing some of the fears they have of their upcoming move to middle/junior high school. If you wish, you can give them to eighth graders who have agreed beforehand to answer them. Or, you can announce that they will not actually be distributed to any older students. Whatever you decide, guarantee privacy. The young people do not have to write their names on the papers. You may ask permission to collect and read them, but you must guarantee privacy. If you choose to ask some trustworthy eighth graders to answer these private letters, set aside group time to talk about the answers when your kids have received their responses. (You can number the letters and ask the kids to remember their numbers, or they can use their birth dates or street address numbers.)

The Discussion:

Item #1: Start this discussion on an exciting note by asking group members to share their thoughts. Record these for all the group to see. You can refer to these later in the discussion when the group becomes preoccupied with the negative.

Item #2: Ask the kids to list additional concerns in the blank spaces. Have the group members compile a top five list of their biggest worries. Examine all of the concerns the group members identified with a special focus on the top five.

Item #3: Ask the young people how their relationship with Christ and the church may change through middle/junior high school. Take time to dialogue both the ups and the downs of the reported changes. Don't just focus on statements reporting a move away from God.

Item #4: You can have a panel of eighth graders available to answer questions, or you can record all questions to be answered by a panel the following week.

Item #5: These passages focus on transition and spiritual growth. Talk with the students about their transition to the next level of education as an opportunity to grow in their relationship with Christ.

To Close the Session:

After reviewing what has been discussed, describe for the kids what the church (or club) has available for them when they graduate into middle/junior high school. You can ask the middle/junior high school leader of your youth group as well as some members of the youth group to describe on videotape or in person what the next level has in store for them. The group members can also write questions on 3 x 5 cards listing any concerns they may have that can be answered later by their new leadership.

HALLOWEEN HYSTERIA

1. How does your school observe Halloween?

_____

_____

2. In the sentence below, fill in the blank with either the word *want* or the words *not want*.

A kid who is a Christian will _____ to participate in trick-or-treating.

3. What kind of costumes would be appropriate for Christians to wear on Halloween? (Check those that would be appropriate.)

___ None   ___ Skeletons

___ Devils   ___ Cartoon characters

___ Super heroes   ___ Any costume they want

___ Ghosts   ___ Bible characters

___ Movie characters   ___ Witches

4. Halloween has nothing to do with Satan.

___ **I agree**   ___ **I disagree**

5. Make a list of all of the positive and negative aspects of Halloween in the boxes below.

POSITIVE	NEGATIVE

6. Read the following verses and decide what message they have in common.

Leviticus 19:31   2 Kings 17:17   Isaiah 8:19

_____

_____

Date Used: _____

Group: _____

HALLOWEEN HYSTERIA
Topic: Halloween and the Satanic

Purpose of this Session:

Proponents of Halloween generally reflect upon the fun and creativity expressed by children during their school, home, church, and neighborhood celebrations of the event. They argue that a few pumpkins and friendly looking ghosts do not harm kids. Opponents of the holiday counter that Halloween is a day dedicated to the Devil and to evil. They cite examples of satanic symbols, ritual sacrifices, and the like.

The reality, no matter what your position, is that most kids do participate in the holiday whether it be at school or in their neighborhoods. They have seen since their toddler years posters of goblins, skeletons, and witches, and they are likely to continue in their involvement. The purpose of this TalkSheet is to help kids examine what occurs on and right before Halloween from a Christian perspective.

To Introduce the Topic:

Ask the group to create a list of costumes people wear for Halloween. Normally, kids will brainstorm a long list of evil-looking and sinister characters. Keep the list for use during your discussion of Item #3.

The Discussion:

Item #1: Create a list of all the ways kids report celebrating Halloween. Write down things like the kinds of decorations found at their schools and the types of masks worn. Some schools limit the sinister by not allowing kids to have fake blood or wear scary costumes. Ask why this is so. If a local school does not celebrate Halloween, ask the kids what they do. Usually there is some sort of fall or harvest festival or other alternative activity. Explore why kids think there are alternatives. Ask how involved Christians should become in Halloween celebrations.

Item #2: Ask the young people to provide reasons for their responses. Respect the opinions of each child answering. Be sensitive and support the kids whose parents promote alternative activities to replace Halloween. For those kids who believe it is appropriate for a Christian kid to participate in trick-or-treating, ask them to articulate some ground rules for doing so.

Item #3: Refer back to the list of costumes you generated in introducing this session. Ask the group members to identify those costumed characters they feel would be considered evil. Place an X over each of these as kids identify them. Many of the costumes identified will be from horror movies. Spend some time talking about why these movies are so popular. Point out how our culture has confused evil with good through the many horror movies popular today. You may find that your kids have the attitude that evil is not evil if it is fun. And since the movies are fun, they are confused about what evil really is. This confusion carries over into the celebration of Halloween. You may find that the movies your kids have seen have desensitized them to evil. Create a list of costumes appropriate for Christians to wear.

Item #4: Halloween is directly related to the satanic. Historically, October 31 was a witches holiday. The tradition of wearing costumes was derived from a Celtic custom of wearing animal skins to derive power from the animals and the superstitious custom of wearing masks to scare away the evil spirits. Trick-or-treating was derived from a superstitious custom done to break the curses of demons. The emphasis on black cats, ghosts, witchcraft, death, skeletons, horrors, and goblins supports the satanic connection of Halloween. Take this opportunity to teach your kids about the biblical doctrine of Satan and evil.

Item #5: Balance your discussion by talking about both the positive and the negative aspects. Discuss how Christian kids can be involved in Halloween and still please God. Support those kids whose families have chosen not to participate at all. This is one very valid option and should not be put down. Kids will identify candy, dressing up, parties, no homework, and events at school as positive aspects. They will identify strangers, crime, evil costumes, poisoned candy, Devil's night, and tricks as the negative aspects.

Item #6: Each of these passages speaks out against the occult. Many of the activities identified in these passages are celebrated during Halloween.

Young people need to know that satanic activity is not simply a bunch of fun activities. Evil really does exist in this world and it is celebrated on Halloween. Read 1 Peter 5:8 –11 and discuss how Christians can be "self-controlled and alert" in resisting the Devil.

To Close the Session:

Point out that dressing up in a costume and trick-or-treating is not of itself demonic. Some Christians have decided not to participate in any Halloween activities because they feel strongly that this holiday celebrates the satanic and glorifies evil. Others have tried to observe the holiday without giving glory to the sinister. Christians must make some tough choices during the Halloween season concerning how involved they will become.

As Christians, we also want to be witnesses for Christ. If we have a condescending attitude toward others concerning Halloween or appear to unbelievers as exaggerating the horrors of Halloween, we will not be taken seriously. These attitudes can only hurt our kids as they are growing in Christ. Help your kids to see ways they can navigate the Halloween season so they can keep their friends and yet please God by what they do.